FORGIVE
and
LIVE

A 12 session small group workbook
for achieving biblical forgiveness

Beth Hunter

Forgive and Live
by Beth Hunter

Printed in the United States of America

Library of Congress Control Number:
ISBN 1-591609-05-4

Xulon Press
www.XulonPress.com

Xulon Press books are available in bookstores everywhere,
and on the Web at www.XulonPress.com.

CONTENTS

ACKNOWLEDGMENTS

There are so many people who have helped me through the process of birthing this book. There is no way that I can name all those who have helped, encouraged and spurred me on. I will do my best to acknowledge those who gave the most time and energy.

First, a big thank you to Donna Tanner who co-lead groups. She spent many hours brainstorming, studying, advising and typing. I could not have done this without her.

Pam Truax also spent many hours helping draft the study, deciding which parts should go where and giving a participant's perspective.

Thanks to Carole Cook who spent time reading the first drafts when I had no idea of what I was doing. She was willing to take the time to argue all the theology and make sure everything lined up with scripture.

Katherine Allen is really responsible for getting it all started. After leaving private practice and feeling that my education was being wasted, Katherine asked me to lead a group for her ministry on forgiveness. This group became my therapy, my outlet from mothering pre-schoolers and homeschooling. I lead groups for two years when suddenly no one showed up. I thought about writing the book and Katherine was so encouraging and has been a resource for the study to spread.

Jillian Gibson also deserves a big thank you for drawing the tree in Week 4, adding additional information to make the instructions more clear and for her servant heart.

I really appreciate the work that Anne Sych did designing the website. She did a terrific job!

Thanks to Matt and Kelly Muhonen, Diane Barton and Briana Reilly for editing my choppy writing. They have smoothed the wrinkles in this work that desperately needed ironing.

Thanks to Billy Coffin who spent many hours typing to save my tired wrists.

The biggest thank you goes to my husband, Rich. He has been my biggest supporter and encourager. He pushed me in places I was too afraid to go and assured me it would work. Most of all, he taught me how to ask for forgiveness and freely forgive another.

INTRODUCTION

Over ten years ago I was seeking a focus for my master's thesis. Throughout my study, the one topic that seemed most important was the one lacking the most resources—forgiveness. I knew it was the key to healing, but none of my classes taught about the issue, much less addressed how to lead a client through forgiveness. Thus I began the research.

My goal was to find a good definition of forgiveness and to develop a practical format for leading someone through the process of forgiveness. It started as a thesis project, went to seminars and retreats, and developed into a 6-8 week lecture/discussion group. Many people said that I should write a book. My response was, "I'm a speaker, not a writer." Finally, God had to arrange my circumstances by not allowing anyone to sign up for a group, giving me the free time to write the book. I was originally planning on an ordinary book with a workbook to accompany it. However, I found many books on forgiveness but very few Bible studies on the subject. Thus I changed the format from a lecture/teaching study to an inductive Bible study where each individual has to dig out for him/herself the riches of Scripture pertaining to forgiveness. This is the culmination of that effort. It has been tried on several groups and I am amazed at the life-changing response that is happening as a result of this study. People are finding freedom in ways they never had with the lecture method.

I hope you will do the homework faithfully and honestly, as others have done, to get the most from this study. I know there will be change and freedom if you do.

Beth Hunter

FORGIVE
and
LIVE

Workbook

FOUNDATIONS OF FORGIVENESS

In order to begin the process of forgiveness, one must understand the foundations of forgiveness, what forgiveness is, and what it is not. This section will outline the misconceptions of forgiveness and offer a definition of forgiveness, providing a foundation for the rest of the study.

MISCONCEPTIONS OF FORGIVENESS

Our family backgrounds, experiences, religious affiliations and culture all influence the way we view forgiveness. Many have rejected forgiveness because they have seen a forgiving person in their lives repeatedly get taken advantage of, used, and abused. They have vowed never to let those things happen to them. Others confuse forgiveness with a lack of consequences. Another portion value forgiveness, but think it is only for those who have experienced terrible tragedy in their lives. Finally, there is the group that believes if you haven't forgotten you haven't forgiven.

Forgiveness is not tolerating the behavior. God does not tolerate our wrong behavior. He is merciful, but He is also just and is not afraid to deal with our sin. He holds us accountable for our behavior and will not let us continue it indefinitely. Remember, Noah built the ark because God would not tolerate the sin in the world. Later, there was Sodom and Gomorrah. (Genesis 13) The whole reason for Christ's death was because God could not and will not tolerate sin. There is a price to pay for sin and it will not go uncollected.

Forgiveness is not excusing the person because of their personality, addictions, or other life circumstances. God never excuses our sin. He is compassionate and loving, but still expects us to follow his commands. David could have used every excuse in the book when he committed adultery with Bathsheba and murdered her husband: "After all, I am the king. I was lonely. She was taking a bath on her roof where everybody could see. I just couldn't help myself. Uriah didn't really love her. If he did, he wouldn't have slept on *my* doorstep when I brought him home. He'd have been with her."

God knew all those possible justifications and excuses going on in David's head, but He did not excuse David. Instead, He sent Nathan to David with a story—one that David would find inexcusable—to confront David with his sin. (II Samuel 12) When David confessed his sin, God forgave him, but there were still consequences for his behavior.

Forgiveness is not minimizing or denying the hurt. If it doesn't hurt, there is nothing to forgive. There is no offense if the behavior is not offensive. We tend to push down our pain for many reasons. We are often too proud, too strong, or too "godly" to feel hurt. But God, who has reason to be proud because He is omnipotent and holy, is still hurt by our sinful behavior. Throughout the Bible, God uses His prophets to express His hurt, pain and disappointment when mankind chooses to go our own way instead of His.

Forgiveness is not forgetting. It is physically impossible to forget a painful event. When a painful event occurs in our lives, it literally makes a mark on our brain. The more painful the event, the deeper the mark. The more we return to that event in our mind, the deeper the groove gets. We can't erase the groove by our own will. It will never be totally gone. However, we can train our brain to have a different response to the event, and that's what forgiveness is all about. Just as when a deep wound heals, a scar is left, but the hurt is gone.

So, what is forgiveness? There are four components that hinge on one another in order for forgiveness to be complete. We must cancel their debt (sin), give up our right to hurt back, trust that God is just and will bring them to repentance. 1) Forgiveness is the cancellation of a debt. Jesus told a story of forgiveness in which a man owed a great deal of money (Matt. 18:21-35). His parable is really about a debt of sin. When we sin against one another, we are in debt to each other and to God. Sin is anything that misses the mark of loving God and loving others (Matt. 22:37-40). If there is no sin, then there is nothing to forgive.

2) Forgiveness is giving up the right to hurt back. Hurting back is based upon the Old Testament "eye for eye, tooth for tooth" (Ex. 21, Deut. 19:21). If you kill my lamb, you have to give me one of yours. If you kill me, your life will be taken as well. Whatever harm you wish for me, I have a right to do to you. I have a right to hurt back, but I choose to give up that right.

How do I give up that right? 3) By trusting that God is just. Our sense of justice is very skewed. We tend to have mercy in areas that we struggle with, but judge more harshly in areas where we have been hurt. When others have wronged someone in the same way we have wronged others, we tend to excuse, justify and rationalize the behavior. "It wasn't that bad. We all make mistakes. Doesn't everybody do that?" But when other's sins hurt us, we do not excuse, justify or rationalize. Instead, we judge quite harshly. "How could they do that? I would never do such a thing. They should be locked away for an eternity for that." God's judgment, however, is not skewed because He is perfect and holy. He sees clearly the nature of the sin and the heart's motives. We can only guess at justice and we are always biased to the situation, but God judges each situation justly.

Unlike man's vengeance, God's discipline is always to 4) bring the offender to repentence. In the Old Testament, we find that Israel is constantly getting into trouble. In the book of Judges alone, each chapter begins with "again the Israelites did evil in the eyes of the Lord." Each time, the Lord's discipline comes to Israel through the invasion of another oppressing nation. God's heart in each situation is saying, "My children, you are going the wrong way and the path that you are following is a deadly one. I will let you taste some of the danger so that your eyes will be opened to see the peril ahead. Then you will repent (turn around) and come back to me and live in safety." When God brings discipline, He is not cruel or vindictive. He motivates the offender to repent. God loves us so much that He will do whatever it takes to bring us back to Him.

There is, however, a judgment, which is final and vindictive. Justice must be carried out. A price must be paid for sin. God alone has the authority to make right a wrong and He will do it. In the end, all of us will stand before the judgment seat of God. Believers allow God to pay the price for their sin through the blood of Christ, but their <u>works</u> will be judged by fire. The behavior that is sinful will burn like wood, hay and stubble, but that which is righteous will survive (I Cor. 3:10-15). Those who are not partakers of salvation will be judged for their sins and thrown in the lake of fire (Rev. 20:15). This may sound harsh, but they chose to pay the price for their own sin. The unrepentant will receive their due judgment, but God, the Righteous Judge, will be the one exacting the judgment. He is the only just Judge.

When we forgive, we are acknowledging that we have been sinned against and that the offender owes us. We give up the right to get back what is owed us and trust God to take care of the offender and the offense. To illustrate this point, let me tell you a story. My grandfather, a short, graying, righteous German, owned his own business making furniture for a living. One particular customer refused to pay for his furniture. Papa sent bills and confronted him many times, with no results. Finally, my grandfather went to the man and told him, "You know that you owe me money, but I am going to take this off my accounts. The matter is now between you and the Lord." I was never told that the man was a believer, yet God must have done a work in him. Seven years later the man paid the bill. Papa had given up his right to collect the money and trusted God to take care of it. God did!

WHAT DO WE FORGIVE?

Whenever forgiveness is mentioned in the Bible, it is always in the context of sin. We don't forgive misunderstandings; we gain understanding. We don't forgive accidents; we overlook them. We don't forgive unrealistic expectations; we lower our expectations. What we forgive is sin.

IS FORGIVENESS AN EVENT OR A PROCESS?

You may be asking, "How long will this forgiveness take? Is it instantaneous, or is this a process that will take a long time?" The answer is yes to both questions. It is instantaneous because it is a choice we make. God calls us to forgive regardless of our feelings. However, forgiveness is also a process, because feelings are involved and a process is required to sort through those feelings. That process may take five minutes or five years, depending upon the depth of hurt, how long ago the offense took place and how much energy has been spent either trying to avoid the memory or nurse the wound.

The process is like a journey. It begins when you get hurt, and you just want to drive as far from the pain as fast as possible. Then you pick up a hitchhiker called Unforgiveness to give you some company. After a while, you get tired and ask Unforgiveness if he'll drive for a while. He readily agrees and takes off fast and furiously. He picks up his friends Revenge, Depression and Bitterness and takes you through dangerous neighborhoods, into the wilderness, over mountains, and through deserts. You want to take over the wheel, but Unforgiveness will not give it up. Only when you are willing to abandon the comfort and security of your vehicle will you be free from your seedy companions. Forgiveness is making the choice to get out of the car and begin the long trek home. It may take you a while to get there, depending on how far you have ridden with Unforgiveness and company, but once you are out of the car, you have begun the journey home.

Furthermore, forgiveness is a lifetime challenge. It is a challenge of learning the skill of forgiveness so that it comes quickly, easily and continually. Because we live in a fallen world with fallen people, we are sinned against on a daily basis. We cannot keep up with all these offenses, so we hang on to some and others we let slip away. We need to develop the skill of forgiving so that we no longer hold on to the offenses, but instead give them to the Father quickly. It takes practice. Just like any other skill, the more we practice, the better we become until forgiveness is not just a skill, but a lifestyle. As we grow in the lifestyle of forgiveness, we begin to go through the process of forgiveness before our defenses drag us into bitterness and resentment. Accounts are kept short and our hearts remain soft.

We are about to embark on a spiritual journey that will take us through many mountains, valleys, deserts and green pastures. Our first stop on our itinerary is to look at unforgiveness and the consequences of it. From there we will spend two weeks expanding our view of forgiveness through studying restoration and boundaries. Then we will begin the six steps of forgiveness. Step One, Examining the Hurt, will take several weeks as we cover self-examination, anger with God, and guilt. The next five steps are Seeking God's Forgiveness, Becoming Other-Centered, Forsaking Revenge, Desiring Restoration and Confrontation.

The format of this study is different from most. Each day will include a brief introduction and then passages of Scripture to read. Three types of questions will be asked about the passages you read. The first type of question is, "What does it say?" Answers will come directly from Scripture. Using the New International Version of the Bible will be helpful for these questions. The second type of question is, "What does it mean?" This type involves a little more thought on your part about the meaning of the passage. The third type is, "What does it mean to me?" These questions are application questions and there are no right or wrong answers. The application questions are the most important ones because they are the life-changing ones. You will be challenged, enlightened, enraged, and assured throughout this study.

WHAT HAPPENS WHEN WE DON'T FORGIVE?

DAY 1—WHO'S THE JUDGE?

Unforgiveness can be a comfortable ally. We hold onto unforgiveness because we believe that it gives us power and that we will lose out if we give up the unforgiveness. There are several benefits that we believe we have with unforgiveness. First, we believe that unforgiveness gives us power—the power to make our offender pay; to make them see that what they did was wrong; and to make them change their behavior and their hearts.

The second benefit we assume is that we have protection in our unforgiveness. Even the idea of forgiveness can be repulsive if we believe that it will open us up to more hurt. Unforgiveness, we believe, will build a protective barrier around our heart and warn us of upcoming danger so we will not be caught unaware again.

Our hearts tell us that unforgiveness is our friend, but scripture tells us that it is our worst enemy. It does not give us power but weakens us, making us vulnerable to spiritual enemies who wound and destroy. Unforgiveness does not protect us. It hardens our hearts to God and to others we love, thus keeping them at a distance and leaving us cold, lonely and afraid.

This week we are studying the root issues and resulting problems of unforgiveness. Today we will focus on the effect of unforgiveness and how it is connected to our relationship with God.

1. What does a judge do? (Think of a court of law.)

2. What are the requirements of a judge?

3. What circumstances can disqualify him/her from judging a case?

A judge is required to be just and fair, not to favor one side over the other. If a judge has a relationship with either party, he is required to excuse himself from the case because he could be biased and unfair. Read Matthew 7:1-2 and James 4: 11-12.

4.   Whose job is it to judge?

5.   What is the danger in judging another?

6.   Why aren't we supposed to judge?

7.   Why is God allowed to judge? (See also Ps. 51:4)

Read Romans 2:1-4.

8.   What are some consequences of judging others?

9.   How does judging others affect our relationship with God?

When we get angry because our offender receives a blessing, it is just like slapping God in the face because it is showing contempt for His kindness.

10.   How does Romans 2:1-4 correlate to Matthew 25:31-46?

When we sit in judgment, we lose not only our connection with God, but also our compassion for mankind. We become so self-focused with making sure that others pay and we don't get hurt, that we refuse to be softened by compassion.

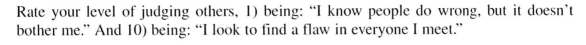

Rate your level of judging others, 1) being: "I know people do wrong, but it doesn't bother me." And 10) being: "I look to find a flaw in everyone I meet."

1———2———3———4———5———6———7———8———9———10

Rate your level of compassion for others, 1) being: "I believe people get exactly what they deserve." And 10) being: "I can lend a helping hand to anybody, no matter what their past has been."

1———2———3———4———5———6———7———8———9———10

God cares about each of his creations, especially each person whom He created in His own image. (Jeremiah 29:11) Although He longs to be with us, we cannot be in His presence because none of us are perfect like God Himself. (Romans 3:23) Even deep within our hearts, before we ever commit a sinful act, we are not holy like God. (Jeremiah 17:9) God must reward us according to what we deserve. (Jeremiah 17:10) Our sins deserve death. (Romans. 6:23)

But God, in His abounding love, didn't want to see that happen. He made a way to bypass judgment and have eternal life. John 3:16 says that God's heart for us is love and wholeness. His gift to us is eternal life because Jesus took the death that we deserved upon Himself. John 1:14 says that in the fullness of His grace He has given us blessings one after another and the greatest of these is Jesus.

To start a relationship with Jesus, all you need to do is to acknowledge that you have done things your own way. Then ask Jesus to forgive you and to become the leader of your life. Have you done this? _____ If so, when? _____ If not, would you like to now? ____ All you have to do is pray this simple prayer:

Dear Jesus, I believe that You are God's Son, that You came to earth, lived a perfect life and died on the cross for my sins. I believe that you rose again on the third day and are now in heaven. I know I have lived life my own way and done things that You have said are wrong. Please forgive me and be the leader of my life. I am now choosing to live life Your way instead of mine. Please help me. Amen

DAY 2—WHO'S GOT YOU?

Yesterday we looked at who has the right to judge. Today we will look more at why we earnestly desire to be the judge. Adam and Eve started it for us and we've followed in their footsteps ever since. Read Genesis 3:1-7.

1.   What was Eve's temptation? (See verses 5-6.)

2.   When we are tempted to judge, how is that like Eve's temptation?

3.   What were Satan's tactics? (See verse 1 and 5)

4.   With Eve, Satan planted seeds of doubt about God's goodness and accused God of withholding something good from her. What does Satan tell you to keep you from forgiving? (I.e. If you forgive, they'll get away with it; they won't think that what they did was wrong; they won't think it hurt; they'll do it again.)

5.   Satan is a scam artist. He never promises to give without taking _more_ in return. What has unforgiveness cost you?

Read Matthew 6:14-15

6.   How does unforgiveness affect our relationship with God?

7.   Does it draw us close to Him, take us away from Him, or have no effect on our relationship with Him at all?

8. Why does God's forgiveness of us hinge on our forgiveness of others? (Hint: Think about Eve's temptation.)

Unforgiveness is a big issue for God. Judging another person is like telling God, "You are not doing a good enough job, so I am taking over. I will be God on this one and I'll show You a thing or two." He does not appreciate the help and will let us walk in the delusion that we can do the job until we become desperate and exhausted. It is not until we give up the revenge that God steps in and does the work that He intended. He cannot and will not act until we are out of the way.

When God says He won't forgive us if we don't forgive others, I don't believe it means that we have lost our salvation. It means that our fellowship with Him is broken because He cannot forgive the sin of unforgiveness while we are unrepentant and feeling justified in our unforgiveness.

Unforgiveness not only breaks our relationship with God, but also ties us to our offender. We carry the offender with us wherever we go. It is like the man in the old west that carried the woman across a river because she had lost her wagon on the trail. She scratched, clawed and complained about her dress getting wet the whole way across. After depositing his burden on the other side, he complained about this ungrateful woman the rest of the trip until someone told him he was still carrying her. He was not focusing on God, how he could be used in this life, or even on the beautiful country that surrounded him. He was tied to her emotionally and spiritually until he let go of her. Whom are you tied to?

DAY 3—WHO DO YOU LOVE?

People are funny. I have heard folks say, "I just love everybody," and not 5 minutes later heard them complaining about people's behavior. We like the idea of love and the "niceness" that it brings, especially in church where everybody is supposed to love. Actually practicing love is hard and usually not fun. It takes a lot of spiritual heart surgery to love because once humans grow past 18 months, we aren't very lovable anymore. Today we will focus on the condition of our hearts and our capacity to love. Read Matthew 12:33-37 and James 3:9-12.

1. How can you tell the attitude of another person's heart?

2. Can anyone ever truly say, "I didn't mean what I said"?

3. Think about the things that come out of your mouth. Rate the sweetness that comes from your mouth, 1) being: "Sword and daggers come from my mouth." And 10) being: "My words are a cool refreshment."

1———2———3———4———5———6———7———8———9———10

Read I John 4:7-21

4. What is love? v. 10

5. Why should we love each other? v. 11-12

6. What gives us the ability to love each other? v. 13-16

7. Can we love God and hate another human? v. 20

8. Can you have love and fear at the same time? v. 18

9. Who are you afraid of?

10. If we are controlled by fear, we not only punish our offender, but everyone else who have the potential to offend us. Who are you punishing that you love? Who are you punishing that you hate?

Since we cannot hate our neighbor, family members or offenders and love God, we cannot hold onto unforgiveness and expect intimacy with the Father. If you have always wondered what has held you back from growing in the Lord, hearing His voice and enjoying His presence, unforgiveness is probably the block. Is unforgiveness worth the cost?

DAY 4—WHO'S AT THE DOOR?

Yesterday we learned some consequences of unforgiveness and how it affects our relationships. In continuing with the same theme, today we will focus on the spiritual impact it has on us. Read Matthew 18:21-35.

1. What was the comparison in the size of debt?

2. What does unforgiveness do to those around us? (See v. 31.)

3. What did the master call the unforgiving servant and why? (See v. 32.)

4. What was the result of his unforgiveness? (See v. 34.)

5. Before the master forgave the servant of his huge debt, his unforgiveness was going to affect everyone and everything associated with this servant. Who is your unforgiveness affecting?

6. This parable is a picture of how God handles unforgiveness. Who is the jailer that He hands us over to?

7. There is a correlation between unforgiveness and cancer, burnout and migraine headaches. How are you being tortured by unforgiveness?

Read II Corinthians 2:10-11.

8. How are we joining hands with Satan when we refuse to forgive?

Unforgiveness has some dangerous ramifications emotionally, physically and spiritually. It causes us to turn our backs on God and link hands with our enemy Satan, who promises us the world, but leaves us imprisoned and tortured. Each of us holds the key to our jail cell. We can escape at any time through the act of forgiveness. Are you ready to be free?

DAY 5—WHO'S IN CONTROL?

In the previous days of this week, we have seen the dangers of unforgiveness and why there is such a great focus of this issue in the Bible. Read Ephesians 4:26-32.

1. According to verse 26 is anger a sin?

2. How can we sin in our anger?

3. What happens when we hold on to anger?

4. What are we stealing from others when we are angry?

5. Ephesians 5 & 6 describe what our relationships on earth should look like as Christians. Paul then gives us some tools to help us in these relationships. Go to Ephesians 6:10-18. What gives us the power to not sin in our anger?

6. If we are believers, we are dressed in the armor of God. Christ is our righteousness. We have the gospel, our faith and our salvation. The word of God is the sword, but just holding it doesn't do us much good. We must use it. What else do we need to do? (v. 13, 14 & 18)

7. How well are you using your sword?

8. So, if our job is to stand and to pray, who's fighting the battle?

9. Who's fighting your battle—you or God?

Forgiveness is all about letting God fight your battle. We will never be able to win the war or even fight effectively if we as privates are trying to do the job of the General. He may still command us to fight, but it will probably not be in the way that we expect to gain results. As privates, we are not privy to the strategy or even all the goals along the way. Throughout the rest of this study we will be learning the job of a private, gaining a little of the General's perspective, and finding the way to freedom.

RESTORATION

Does forgiving someone mean I have to be their best friend? No! There is a difference between forgiveness and restoration. Forgiveness is totally dependent upon the victim choosing to forgive. It is the victim's responsibility, regardless of whether or not the offender repents. Repentance is the responsibility of the offender, even if there is no forgiveness granted. Restoration is dependent upon the victim's forgiveness *and* the offender's repentance. Without both forgiveness and repentance, there can be no restoration. When forgiveness is granted but the person has not repented, the relationship will break. When the offender has repented but the victim refuses to forgive, the relationship will break. The break may not be total. It may be just one broken strand in the cord that ties the relationship together. However, the more offenses that go unforgiven and the longer the offender goes unrepentant, the more strands break until the relationship is hanging by a thread.

The highest goal is restoration. Restoration is to return to a changing/repentant relationship in order that it may become deeper and healthier than before the hurt. When a relationship has gone through a cycle of offense, repentance and forgiveness, the result of the restoration is a stronger relationship than what previously existed. It is similar to a broken bone. When a bone has been broken, then properly set and healed (which takes time), the place in the bone where the break occurred is the strongest part of the bone.

Regret will not aid restoration. Regret says, "You should get over it . . . I'm sorry I got caught . . . I'm sorry you got hurt." Regret does not admit wrongdoing or take responsibility. Thus, the likelihood of a repeat occurrence is not only probable; it is inevitable. Repentance, on the other hand, involves brokenness. Sin is recognized, responsibility is taken, and help is sought. Reoccurrence of the offense may happen, but confession should quickly follow.

When Mary and her husband bought their first home it was brand-new. They got to pick the carpet color and the pattern of linoleum. They chose a creamy white carpet and a sophisticated marble print for the kitchen and foyer. The walls were nice and clean and there was nothing old, smudged or worn out from previous owners. The only thing missing was grass. Because of the weather, the builder had not been able to landscape the yard. The entire yard was still mud with many puddles of standing water. In fact, it was so muddy outside that no one could get from their car to the house without getting mud on their shoes.

Soon after they moved in, Mary's friend Gina wanted to come and see the house. As Gina walked up the sidewalk, she noticed all the mud and thought how difficult it would be to keep new floors clean with such a mess outside. While Gina waited for Mary to come to the door, she saw the cute porcupine mud scraper for shoes that had a sign saying, "Use Me." Gina looked at her shoes. They were brand-new and expensive. If she used the mud scraper, her shoes might get scratched because the leather was so soft. "Besides," she thought, "I couldn't have that much mud on my shoes."

Mary was excited to show off her new house that she had decorated with such loving care and was happy to see Gina when she arrived. Mary took Gina on a tour of the house and showed her each and every room. After every room had been inspected, they went into the kitchen for coffee and muffins. They had a wonderful visit, full of conversation and fellowship. When the visit ended, Mary walked Gina out onto the porch and watched her friend drive away. As she turned to go into the house, she noticed all the mud on the porch. When she went inside to get a broom to clean up the porch, she saw, to her horror, that mud was tracked through her entire house. She was upset to see that her new, creamy white carpet was covered with mud. Mary cleaned it up as best she could, but it was still a mess.

The next day when Gina came back by to visit, Mary met her at the door and requested that Gina take off her shoes before coming in the house. Mary explained her request by saying that mud was tracked throughout the house yesterday because of the muddy condition of her front yard.

There are two scenarios this story could now take. Gina could say, "There is no way I'm taking off my shoes to come into your house." She could have a hole in her sock or have very bad foot odor and be embarrassed to take off her shoes. (We justify our lack of repentance in so many ways.) Then Mary can say, "I'm very sorry that you feel that way, but I cannot let you in the house. I would love for you to come in and have some coffee and talk, but I can't let you in unless you take off your shoes. If you won't take off your shoes, we can stay out on the porch and talk, but it won't be nearly as comfortable, the coffee will cool faster and the fellowship will not be as sweet."

However, if Gina is repentant, she could say, "I am so sorry. I knew I should have used the mud scraper to get the mud off my shoes. Let me help you clean it up. Or, better yet, let me pay to have it professionally cleaned for you. I will be happy to take off my shoes. (Please excuse the hole in my sock.) Let's go inspect the damage."

Our heart is like our home. When people sin against us, it is like tracking mud through the interior of our heart. If there is no repentance, we are not required to let them track mud through our heart again and again. We can stand in the doorway of our heart offering forgiveness, but at the same time creating a boundary if there is no repentance. Without repentance, the relationship deteriorates to fellowship at the doorway of our hearts where it is not as comfortable, the coffee cools faster, and the fellowship is not as sweet. But at that moment of repentance, we need to be ready to at least let them into the foyer.[1]

DAY 1—CHARACTERISTICS OF REPENTANCE -THE HEART OF DAVID

Remember that restoration takes the effort of two people. It involves the forgiveness of the offended and the repentance of the offender. Today we will take a look at what repentance looks like using David as our example.

SEVEN CHARACTERISTICS OF TRUE REPENTANCE

1. A broken and contrite heart.

2. A willingness to take responsibility for one's own behavior. This includes being specific about the sin, owning it and expecting consequences. (In the case of affairs, one does not need to give explicit details to be specific. Being specific means calling the behavior for what it is without justification.)

3. A willingness not to offend again, to do whatever it takes not to offend again, and to submit to another for help to change.

4. Not motivated out of self-pity nor a martyr syndrome. Statements like, "It's always my fault;" "I'm such a failure;" "I can't ever do anything right;" are really excuses not to change or to take responsibility.

5. Does not place guilt or blame onto the one offended—they realize that no matter the actions or inactions of others, each person is responsible for their own behavior.

6. Not motivated out of anger, but humility—there is no resentment about having to confess a wrong.

7. Claims no rights while asking mercy for a wrong done.

Psalm 51 and II Samuel 12 record the repentance and confession of David after he was confronted for his adultery with Bathsheba and the murder of her husband. Read these passages and summarize how David displayed each characteristic.

1. David showed a broken and contrite heart by—

2. David showed he was willing to take responsibility for his behavior by—

3. David showed he didn't want to offend again by—

4. David showed his repentance was not out of self-pity nor a martyr syndrome by—

5. David showed he would not shift the blame by—

6. David showed his repentance was not out of anger, but humility by—

7. ·David showed he would claim no rights while asking mercy for a wrong done by—

When some of you think about repentance in light of your offender, it is a foreign concept. Others have heard some semblance of repentance, but it seems empty. Compare the above characteristics with the repentance of your offender. Has true repentance occurred?

Now compare these characteristics with your repentance when you have sinned against another. How do you measure up?

DAY 2—JOSEPH'S TESTING

The restoration process involves several steps. The steps include 1) **testing repentance**, 2) **building trust**, 3) **reaffirmation of love** 4) **stopping the sandbagging** and 5) **resuming the relationship**. Today we will study the first step of **testing the repentance** of the offender. There is a lot of reading today, but since it is a familiar story it should go quickly. Joseph is our example. Read Genesis 37, 41:41-45:28, and 50:15-21.

1. Why didn't Joseph's brothers recognize him? (See Genesis 37:2, 41:14-46 and 42:23.)

2. Why did Joseph want Benjamin brought to him? Check all that apply.
    ___ He was his only full brother, thus the next favored one.
    ___ He wanted to torment his father.
    ___ He wanted to get his brothers into trouble.
    ___ He wanted to see how the brothers treated him.

3. How did he test the brothers? Check all that apply.
    ___ He continued to favor Benjamin, testing the brothers' jealousy.
    ___ He saw who would sacrifice themselves for Benjamin.
    ___ He gave them a pop quiz.
    ___ He put them in a chariot race.

4. How do we know that Joseph had already forgiven them? (See Genesis 43:23, 45:7-8, and 50:19-20.)

5. Was Joseph malicious in his testing? How do we know?

6. How have you tested your offender's repentance?

7. Were you malicious in your testing?

DAY 3—HOW GOD BUILT TRUST WITH GIDEON

After testing repentance comes **building trust**. Whenever a relationship has been vio-
lated, trust has been broken. Usually it is not just on one side, but on both. Neither party
feels they can trust the other. This phenomenon does not just happen in our human relationships. It also happens with God. Even though we are not supposed to test God, we
seem to have a need to do so because we tend to compare God to the humans we know.
Today we are going to look at a fearful warrior who became a great leader because he
learned to trust. Let's read Judges 6.

1.   Where was Gideon when God found him?

2.   What did God call Gideon?

3.   What did God command Gideon to do?

4.   What was Gideon's reply?

5.   What was God's answer to Gideon's excuses?

6.   What are some reasons Gideon might not have trusted God?

7.   What was Gideon afraid of?

8.   What did God do to build trust with Gideon?

9.   Gideon asked God for a sign not once or twice, but three times. Name the signs
      Gideon received.

Did God get angry? Did God leave the relationship because Gideon wouldn't give him
automatic trust? Praise God, no! God is patient with us as we test Him to learn how trustworthy He really is.

10.   What kind of sign are you looking for from God before you will trust Him?

Even though God had not sinned against Gideon, He was still willing to do His own part in building trust. We too have a responsibility to regain our offender's trust. We have to prove that we will love unconditionally, and when repentance comes, show that we will release them from guilt, condemnation and continual reminders of the past.

11. What are you doing to create an atmosphere of trust with your offender?

12. What are you doing to create an atmosphere of distrust with your offender?

DAY 4—HOW GIDEON BUILT TRUST WITH GOD

Mankind often tests God's trustworthiness. God's trust does not deserve to be tested because He "is not a man that He should lie" (Num. 23:19). Humans are a different story. God knows this and tests us to determine our level of trustworthiness. He knows both our potential for good and for evil. As we are watching to see if God can be trusted, He is doing the same to us. As we build trust with our offender, the bridge is built from both sides of the chasm. Today, let's read Judges 6:25-7:25 to see how God was testing Gideon's level of trustworthiness.

1. God asked Gideon to do several things. What were they?

2. Was God testing Gideon's ability? If not, what was He testing?

God is not concerned about our ability. Usually, whatever He calls us to do is beyond our ability anyway. This way, we learn to rely on *His* ability. When we are weak, He is strong (II Corinthians 12:10). God's test is a test of obedience.

3. What are you asking of your offender that he/she thinks is beyond their ability?

4. God understood Gideon's fear about completing the task assigned and gave him encouragement that he would succeed. How can you encourage your offender that success is within reach?

5. What has God asked you to do in reference to your offender that is beyond your ability? Are you willing to obey?

6. First, God asked Gideon to fight the enemy within (the struggle with idol worship) and then to fight the physical enemy. What is your enemy within? What enemy exists outside of yourself?

7. Your offender is not your enemy. Your offender is a prisoner of war. Satan, who has captured your offender and put him in bondage, is the enemy. What can you do to fight the true enemy?

8. How will this help you to build trust with your offender?

DAY 5—A NEW TESTAMENT RESTORATION

We have examined the first 2 steps of restoration, testing repentance and building trust. Today we will explore the third step, **reaffirming love** for the offender. There are 2 situations in our study today. One story is very vivid and the other is kind of vague, just like life. First, let's look at the restoration of Saul and the church.

Initially, Saul and the church were bitter enemies. When Saul was converted and wanted to join the church, the church body was quite skeptical. Let's look at one representative of the church, Ananias, and see how he handled Saul's repentance. Read Acts 9:1-19.

1. Did Ananias hear repentance from Saul?

2. Who told him to go to Saul?

3.   What did God tell him to do for Saul?

4.   Why was Ananias afraid to go?

5.   Why are you afraid to go to your offender?

6.   In whom did Ananias put his trust?

7.   What did Ananias call Saul in verse 17?

8.   What do you think this term of endearment meant to Saul? What would it mean to your offender?

Let's look at another restoration. Read II Cor. 2: 5-11.

9.   Was the sin dealt with or ignored?

10.   Was the person repentant?

11.   Why did Paul say to forgive and comfort the man?

12.   What did Paul urge them to do?

13.   What was the purpose in forgiving and restoring? (v. 11)

14.   In both situations there is a reaffirmation of love for the offender, even when there was no love lost between the parties. This is an important step in restoration so that one person does not become "overwhelmed by excessive sorrow." What are you doing to reaffirm your love for your repentant offender?

The fourth step in restoration is to **stop sandbagging**. Sandbagging means to continually rehash the offense, especially in times of crisis. The motive is usually to keep the offender feeling guilty so that he/she will not offend again. It doesn't work and only leads to more strife. The offense should be discussed in the future, but not during arguments or crises. The discussions should be more of a remembrance of what God has taken you through as a testimony of His powerful healing.

The fifth step, **resuming the relationship**, really must come first. If it does not, there will be no opportunities to test repentance, to build trust, or to reaffirm love. We must provide these opportunities in order for the relationship to attain the status it was before the event. Once the test of repentance has been passed, trust has been built, and love has been reaffirmed, then the end result is a stronger relationship than there was before.

BOUNDARIES

Restoration is God's goal, but what if the offender is not repentant? Are we to restore the relationship anyway? Boundaries established by the victim are appropriate when repentance does not occur. Boundaries are biblical whether the boundaries are physical, emotional or spiritual.

The Thessalonians were instructed to stay away from those who did not heed Paul's instructions (2 Thes. 3:14-15). The Corinthian church was told to excommunicate a man who was living with his father's wife (I Cor. 5). Matthew 18 gives us guidelines for boundaries in relationships. Only after we have followed the steps of confrontation with no repentance are we to cut off the relationship with our offender. The purpose is not to be mean and vindictive, but to allow the person to experience the consequences of the sin (loneliness and lack of fellowship) in the hope that they will repent (2 Thes. 3:14-15, I Cor. 5:5).

Without forgiveness *and* repentance, the relationship will break in some form or fashion. We are held together by cords of relationship. When the offense is small, one or two strands in the cord that ties the relationship together will break. When the offense is big, many strands will break. This does not give license to chop off the cord that holds the relationship. When the break is only a couple of strands, the fellowship is not as sweet, communication is strained and trust is lacking. A break or boundary in the relationship is not so much for the protection of the victim (although that may be a consideration), as it is for the good of the offender. In establishing a boundary, we are allowing the offender to experience the consequences of his sin in order to draw him to repentance. Without the boundary, there is no consequence. The message sent is that the behavior is okay, and that there was no sin. As a result, the offender may never realize the need for repentance.

For some of us, setting boundaries is difficult because we fear the retribution of our offender or the opinions of others. For others, setting boundaries comes easy because we no longer have to deal with the person who offended us. But boundaries in relationships should grieve us, not relieve us. If putting a boundary in the relationship does not break our hearts, then we need to examine the motive of our hearts.

God places boundaries on us when there is unrepented sin in our lives. He does not answer prayer, He removes his protection, His voice is not as clear, and fellowship with Him is not as sweet. Why does He put these boundaries in place? His boundaries are established so we will realize our sin and repent. It is for our good, not His, that He allows us to experience the consequences of our sin. Does God rejoice over these boundaries? No way! He longs for sweet, intimate fellowship with us and desires to answer our prayers and protect us from all harm. The boundaries grieve Him, but our lack of repentance grieves Him more. This week we will be studying a biblical example of boundaries set between David and Saul.

DAY 1—SETTING THE SCENE

In order to understand the boundaries David set, we must first understand the conflict and the reason for it. We'll start at the beginning and work our way through the story. Saul, Israel's first king, was totally unknown before becoming king. He was simply a lowly farmer who lost his donkeys and went looking for them. Having no luck, his servant suggested going to see Samuel, the prophet, to see if he could tell them where the donkeys were. Samuel then invited Saul to a feast. To find out what happened next, read I Samuel 10-11, 12:12-13:15.

1. How was Saul made king? Check one.
    ___ Hostile takeover
    ___ Election by his peers
    ___ Chosen by God and anointed by Samuel
    ___ Was born a prince

2. Anointed means "set apart." Saul was set apart by God to lead his people. When was Saul made king?

3. What was Saul like in the beginning of the story? What was his attitude towards God?

4. Why was it "evil" for the people to want a king?

5. After Saul was reaffirmed king, what was Samuel's advice to him and the people? (Hint: Check out 12:24-25.)

6. What was Saul's response in Chapter 13?

7. What was his motivation for offering the sacrifice?

8. Why was it wrong for him to offer the sacrifice?

9.   What was the consequence?

Now read I Samuel 15.

10. Why did God reject Saul as king?

11. How important is obedience to God?

12. At what level is your obedience? (1) Being: "I think it is easier to ask for forgiveness than for permission." And (10) being: "I have learned that no matter what, it is better to obey."

1———2———3———4———5———6———7———8———9———10

13. How can you raise your level of obedience?

DAY 2—THE SPIRIT IS PASSED ON

Now that we have an understanding of how Saul gained and lost a kingdom, let's look at the next king, David. Read I Samuel 16:1-14.

1.   How was the anointing of David similar to Saul's?

2.   How was David different from Saul?

3.   What was Samuel looking for in a king?

4. What was God looking for in a king?

5. What does God see when he looks at your heart?

Now Read I Samuel 17:1 through I Samuel 18:9

6. What was Goliath's challenge?

7. What was the response of Saul and the people?

8. What was the response of David?

9. What was the focus of David and what was the focus of Saul?

10. Before this encounter, Saul was dependent on David for his mental stability. Once he commissioned David to fight, for what else did Saul become dependent on David?

11. Why did Saul want David to wear his armor?

12. Why did Saul keep David close to him?

13. What made Saul so jealous of David?

14. Where is your focus—on your circumstances, your enemies, or on the Lord?

DAY 3—GETTING RID OF THE COMPETITION

Saul's son, Jonathan, had accepted that he would never be king so he never saw David as a threat. Instead, David was his ally and best friend. However, Saul knew that the kingdom was going to be ripped from him and his anxiety over that fact grew, along with David's popularity. Soon Saul decided to take matters into his own hands to secure the kingdom for his son who was happy to give it away. Read I Samuel 18:10 through I Samuel 20.

1.   What does David do the first time Saul tries to harm him?

It's incredible to me that David would give Saul the time to retrieve his spear and try again. Even then, David did not leave him.

2.   What was Saul's next tactic to get rid of David?

3.   What did it do for Saul?

4.   How did Saul use his own daughter to try to eliminate David?

5.   In Chapter 19, when Saul promised Jonathan that he would not take David's life, how willing was David to accept Saul at his word?

6.   How willing are you to accept your offender at his or her word?

7.   When Saul proved that his word could not be trusted, David left town. How then did he test the motive of Saul's heart?

8.   What have you done to test your offender's heart?

In the previous chapter we saw how Joseph tested his offenders' repentance and found it true. He was then able to continue the restoration process. David tested Saul's repentance and found it wanting. He did not continue with the restoration process but allowed the relationship to disintegrate, putting distance between himself and his offender. The next day's work will show how David was able to forgive Saul, keeping his heart soft, but still not restoring the relationship.

DAY 4—THE LORD'S ANOINTED

David was able to keep a soft heart toward God and Saul because he had perspective. Read I Samuel 23:15-24:22 to discover that perspective.

1.   Where did David find strength?

2.   Who protected David in the Desert of Maon?

3.   Why was David conscience stricken after cutting off a corner of Saul's robe?

David was remorseful for assaulting even the clothing of the anointed one of God. Saul was anointed in private, as was David. You never know who is anointed of God. You may be thinking, "There is no way my offender can be anointed. He is evil incarnate." However, Saul was possessed by an evil spirit and still anointed of God.

4.   How did David show respect for the anointed one of God?

5.   How are you showing respect for your offender?

6.   Who did David call on to judge?

7.   Look at the characteristics of repentance in Week 2. Did Saul repent?

8.   Where was Saul's focus?

Even though Saul spoke the words of repentance, David stayed in the desert. Read I Samuel 26 to see why this was a good decision.

9.   Why did David go into Saul's camp?

10. How did David expect vengeance to be taken?

11. Did Saul repent this time? (See characteristics of repentance.)

12. In whom did David entrust his life?

Again, the two men parted, never to see each other again. Read II Samuel 1:1-16 to see David's heart for Saul.

13. What was David's attitude towards his offender (Saul)?

14. What was his attitude towards God's vengeance?

15. What is your attitude when you see your offender experiencing the consequences of sin?

Few of us have experienced the life-threatening offense that David did and yet he still grieved over the death of Saul. David had a heart like God's that did not wish any to perish, but all to have eternal life. I believe that he grieved because he knew that Saul died unrepentant and had to face God with his sin between them. The consequences were in eternal dimensions, no longer temporary. The judgment was now final.

If you are still in the place of hoping that your offender will rot in hell forever, this book is for you. Few of us automatically jump to the place David landed in II Samuel 1. David went through a process as well. Just read the Psalms and you will see David's emotional turmoil and the pain he wished inflicted on his offenders. The difference between David and most of the world is that he quickly laid the matter in God's hands, surrendering to His authority and control. But don't despair! The rest of this book will help you to discover how to do that too.

DAY 5—BIBLICAL GUIDELINES TO BOUNDARIES

In ancient times property lines were marked with stones painted white. These boundary stones were like the pegs put in the ground today by surveyors. If a neighbor came in the night and moved a boundary stone 1 inch one day each week, it would hardly be noticed, but in one month he would have stolen 4 inches of property. Over the course of one year, he would have stolen 4 feet! That's a lot of land!

We also have boundaries around our hearts. When people move those boundary stones, it is like they are stealing parts of our hearts! When we push the boundary stones of others, in a sense we are taking over parts of their hearts. Read Deuteronomy 27:17 and Proverbs 23:10-11 to see what the Bible says about boundaries.

1. What will happen to one who moves a boundary stone?

2. Who has encroached on your land?

3. On whose land have you encroached?

Now read Matthew 18:15-17

4. Who are we to confront about sin?

5. Why should we go one-on-one first?

6. Are we told to process our feelings with another before we go?

We must be very careful not to sin against our offender through gossip.

7. If there is no repentance, how should the person be treated?

8.   How should we treat the unsaved?

Read I Cor. 5:5.

9.   Why were they to hand the man over to Satan?

10.   Who do you need to hand over?

Read II Thes. 3:14-15

11.   When should we cut off the relationship?

12.   For what purpose do we cut off the relationship?

13.   What relationship have you cut off?

14.   Did it grieve your heart or relieve your heart?

If it did not grieve your heart, there is some part where self-protection and revenge is the motive. Remember, David grieved for the man who sought to murder him. Take some time to evaluate your own heart. If revenge has been your motive, you are not alone and there is forgiveness. If self-protection has been your motive, we'll discuss that more in a later chapter.

STEP 1—
EXAMINING THE HURT

DAY 1—STARTING HOME

To begin the process of forgiveness we must first **examine the hurt**. This involves identifying what we are forgiving. We need to look at both the ways we have been hurt and the depth of that hurt in order to know what it is that we are forgiving. If there is no hurt, there is no need for forgiveness. This examination may take 5 minutes or 5 years depending on the depth of the hurt, the length of time that has passed since the hurt and how long that hurt has festered.

Remember this is a process, not a linear one, but an upward spiral. Through each step you will find healing, and as you do, it will trigger things from the last step that need attention. You are not moving backwards but forwards with greater depth of healing.

Part of examining the hurt is differentiating between the types of hurt. There are four types: 1) universal hurt, 2) perceived hurt, 3) unrealistic expectations, and 4) self-centeredness. **Universal hurt** is anything that is legally, morally and ethically wrong. In other words, it's sin. In our American culture we do not like to label our actions or the actions of others as "sin" for fear of being viewed as intolerant and judgmental. However, it is important in this step because this is the only hurt where forgiveness is needed. As you examine the behavior of your offender ask yourself, "Is there scripture that speaks to this behavior? Is there a law against this? Is the behavior something that our culture finds offensive?"

That last question is one with which you must be careful. Our culture finds evangelism offensive, yet scripture commands us to do this. One example of a cultural/ethical offense would be serving wine in the presence of someone who struggles with alcoholism. It is not against scripture to serve wine or to drink wine, but it would be sinful to cause another to stumble.

Perceived hurt is one that reminds you of a past hurt that has not yet been healed. Suppose someone stabs you in the arm. That would be a sin. If you wrap that wound in a bandage and never change the dressing it will get infected, gangrene will set in and the whole arm will become very sensitive. If at some time later someone accidentally brushes against that arm, the reaction would be totally out of proportion to the "offense." The reaction is not really a result of the brush, but results from the lack of healing from the stabbing. When you find yourself reacting out of proportion to the offense, ask yourself, "Who has made me feel this way before?" The answer may be parents, teachers, or other authority figures, siblings, previous boyfriends/girlfriends, childhood experiences, or other unresolved conflicts/experiences. There may or may not have been a sin in the brushing incident. If there wasn't, you need to deal with the original wound. If there was a sin, both offenses need to be forgiven.

Unrealistic expectation is the third type of hurt. As you examine the hurt, ask if the expectation was realistic, verbalized and agreed upon. For example, Sue, a stay-at-home mom, went out for a rare evening with friends. She came home to find the kitchen a mess and her husband, Dan, lounging on the sofa. Sue was furious. The least Dan could do was clean the kitchen while she got a few hours break. Did Dan sin against Sue? There are several factors that need to be considered.

1. Did Sue ask Dan to clean the kitchen while she was out?
2. Did Dan agree to complete the task?
3. Were there unforeseen circumstances that kept him from completing the task?

If we stop and think about the reality of our expectations, it will save us a lot of time, energy and heartache. It will also teach us to verbalize our expectations instead of believing others can and should read our minds.

The fourth form of hurt is plain old **self-centeredness**. Our feelings get hurt when we don't get our way: "She didn't make me the head of the committee, he didn't like my idea, I wasn't invited to the party, he interfered with my agenda," etc. This is the form of hurt that we least like to admit, but the one that we experience most often.

Your assignment for today is:

1. Get a journal and make a list of your offenders. Each offender should have a page. For some of you a small binder will do, for others, you need the 5 subject spiral and others need a 3 ring notebook.
2. Choose one offense and under your offender's name, write out what happened to offend you.
3. Write what type of hurt it was.
4. For those hurts that are universal hurts, name the sin. If possible, find a scripture that addresses the behavior or attitude.
5. For the perceived hurts, find the original wound and follow directions for #4.
6. For unrealistic expectations and selfishness, give the hurt feelings to Jesus. (This will be dealt with further in Week 7.)

DAY 2—ANGER—PART I

For many of you, yesterday's assignment stirred up a lot of anger as you remembered some significant hurts from your past, both ancient and recent. Anger walks beside unforgiveness, and for that reason the rest of the week will be devoted to a study on anger.

Everybody has heard the New Testament verse "in your anger, do not sin" but few have noticed that this is a quote from a psalm. Today we are going to study that psalm. Read Psalm 4.

1. What is your distress?

2. Where does your shame come from?

3. Where are you going for comfort and relief from your distress?

4. What should you do with your anger? (second half of v. 4)

Anger is a secondary emotion. This means that when we experience an offense, the first or primary emotion that we feel is some type of hurt or fear. Those vulnerable feelings we tend to cover with the powerful emotion of anger. Sometimes we are so quick to skip to anger that we are unaware of the vulnerable emotions. Therefore, when we feel the anger, God tells us to go to a quiet place and think about why we are angry and what the primary emotion really is in order to deal with that feeling.

5. What is a "right sacrifice?" (See I Sam. 15:22 and Ps. 51:16-17)

6. What does trust have to do with a right sacrifice?

7. Where are you looking for good in your life?

8. How do you get joy?

9. How can you sleep in peace?

Anger robs us of joy, peace and rest. It consumes our energy during the day and keeps us awake at night. Yet sometimes we make friends with our anger. It becomes a comfort, giving us a sense of protection and an illusion of revenge. Tomorrow we will study some scriptures motivating us to give up our friendship with anger.

DAY 3—ANGER REVISITED

Today we are going to a familiar passage about anger in the New Testament. This study will help us see how anger is bad company. Read Ephesians 4:26-32.

1. How do you, personally, sin in your anger?

2. What happens when we hold onto our anger?

3. The New English Version translates verse 27 as "Do not let the sun still find you nursing it." I like the word picture this verse paints. What happens when you feed/nurse a baby?

4. What do you tell yourself that feeds your anger?

There are two general ways to sin in our anger. One is through other-contempt, or the outward expression of anger.

5. Looking at vs. 29-31, what is the most common way your anger is expressed towards others?

6. What are the effects of your anger on others?

7. Read James 1:20. Anger is often used as an effort to change the behavior of others, but it is never effective in the long run. How have you used your anger to change another? What was the result?

The other way to sin in our anger is through self-contempt or anger turned inward. Read Proverbs 10:18.

8. What happens when we hide our anger? Who do we lie to?

9. If it is not O.K. to hide our anger, then can we talk about it to whomever we like?

Although there is a valid need to process our feelings with another, we also need to be careful not to slip into gossip. Gossip can be defined as any words that would cast a shadow on another. If you need to process your feelings with a third party, it is best to do that with someone who does not know the offender, who has the ability to focus on you, your actions and your responses—not those of the offender.

There is a progression to anger. If anger is not dealt with early, it will turn into resentment and then, as it matures, bitterness sets in. Read Hebrews 12:15.

10. What is the word picture of bitterness?

11. Who does bitterness hurt?

12. Look at the diagram of the tree. Identify some seeds and bitter roots in your life and the fruit that have come from them. Seeds would represent hurtful events in your life. Bitter roots would be your negative emotional response to those events. The fruit would be the defense mechanisms, negative coping behaviors, or bad habits that resulted. For example, in my life there was a seed sown in childhood of fickle friends. From this seed grew a bitter root of self-protection. The fruit that came was invulnerability, perfectionism and pride. (This question may take a while to answer. So for today, answer what you can and return to the question as more is revealed to you throughout the study.)

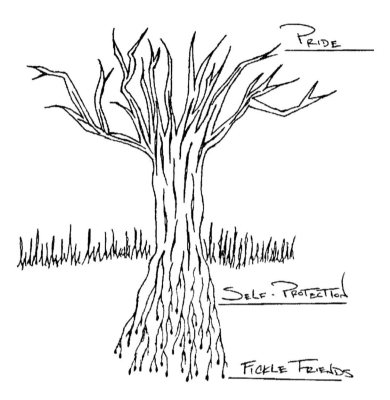

Some fruits of anger are pointed at others like criticism, judging, a bad temper, foul language, gossip, etc. Verbal assault is probably the most common and includes various weapons. Some use a broadsword, browbeating another into the ground. Others use stilettos, jabbing others when they least expect it.

Other fruits of anger are directed at ourselves. This is anger stuffed down and turned inward. The fruit is seen in depression, migraine headaches, cancer, rheumatoid arthritis, etc. Many physical ailments have their root in unresolved anger.

Tomorrow we will see how anger affects not just our relationship with others and our health, but is an indication of a problem in our relationship with God.

DAY 4—THE SPIRITUAL BAROMETER OF ANGER

Anger has a spiritual component in that it can be used as a barometer to expose our relationship with God. Anger indicates that there is not only a problem between me and another person, but between me and God. Remember, anger is a secondary emotion, a barking dog, if you will, and something is making the dog bark. Anger reveals a lack of trust in God to protect, provide, comfort, defend, love or accept. Let's look at three scriptures to illuminate this concept. First read Genesis 4:1-8.

1. What was the difference in Cain and Abel's sacrifice?

2. Why was Cain angry?

3. Who was he really angry with—God or Abel?

4. What was Cain afraid of?

5. What did he do with his fear?

Cain's fear that he would not be loved and accepted stirred his anger and caused him to sin by killing his competition. Now read Exodus 14:1-18 to find what motivated Israel's anger and how they sinned in their anger.

6. Israel has just been delivered from Egypt through the miraculous wonders of God. Where did God tell the Israelites to camp?

7. What did God want Pharaoh to do?

8. Why did God want Pharaoh to pursue them?

9. Who did the Israelites cry out to?

10. Who did they blame?

11. What were they afraid of?

Israel, afraid that God would not protect them, turned their anger against Moses. God delivered them from their fears and even revealed himself to the Egyptians and received glory in the process. But Israel still did not learn to trust God. Read Exodus 16:1-12 to find out what happened just a few weeks later.

12. Who did Israel grumble against?

13. What were they afraid of?

14. Who were they really grumbling against?

15. Was God blind to their need for food?

16. Why did He position them to be in a place of need?

17. What does this passage say about Israel's trust in God?

18. What demands have you placed on God?

Our anger reveals the demands we place not just on others, but primarily the demands we have placed on God. We have certain ideas of the way life is supposed to be. No one we love will ever die, our family will never have a critical illness, there should be no financial difficulties, etc. We will discuss how to deal with anger when life does not go our way in Week 5.

Another source of anger is when our needs are not met the way we want them to be. God is to be the source of our love, security, comfort, provision, and protection. When we feel that those needs are not being met the way we want, we get angry at the one we believe is supposed to supply the need. Usually, our first thought is not God but some human whom we think should meet the need. This is idolatry. The only solution is repentance, turning your eyes back to the real source of our needs and trusting Him to provide.

DAY 5—PRACTICAL APPLICATION

Today will be a summary of everything that you have learned this week. Below are five steps to getting rid of anger. Think of an occurrence which has made you angry and work it through these steps in your journal.

1. Anger is a powerful emotion. It gets our adrenaline going and gives us the energy needed to fight or flee. The first step in resolving anger is to get rid of the energy the anger produces. This can be done by walking, running, lifting weights, beating a pillow, playing racquetball, writing, driving, throwing rocks at a tree in the woods, journaling, worshipping, etc. Some of these things will not work for you. There are others not listed that will work for you. You have to find your own way of getting rid of the energy. Be sure to choose something that is not destructive. This would be sinning in your anger and you'll only have to pay for it in the end. (So no throwing plates, punching holes through walls, speeding, etc!)

2. Find out what event and/or person(s) caused the anger. Did it happen five minutes ago, five hours ago or five years ago? Is the person you are angry at standing in front of you, back at work, on the playground from your childhood, or dead long ago? Identifying the event and person prevents you from taking your anger out on someone who may not have caused it. So write out the event that caused your anger.

3. Find the primary emotion that the anger is covering. Hurt and fear cover a broad range of emotions. There are many subcategories under both hurt and fear. If you have trouble identifying the exact emotion, please see the appendix for a Feelings List. Write down the primary emotion(s) that your anger is covering.

4. Find out how the emotion relates to God. For example, when my husband started his own business, there was a season when he was having difficulty making sales calls, doing marketing, etc. As we were talking about this one night, I began to get very angry. We brainstormed ways to solve the problem, but I was still angry. I even went to bed angry, which is very unusual for me. When I woke up, still angry, I decided it was time to take my own advice and get rid of the anger. When I got to step 3, I found my primary emotion to be fear; fear that he wouldn't make sales calls, he wouldn't make money, we would lose our house, lose our car, and be homeless destitutes on the street. I asked myself, "What does this emotion say about my relationship with God?" The answer was that I was expecting my husband to be my provider and not trusting the Lord as my provider. When I repented of that, my anger disappeared. Write what your primary emotion tells you about your relationship with God.

5. Stop nursing it!! There are times when anger will try to latch back on. Before anger starts tugging at you, analyze your thought processes so that you will be aware of how anger asks to be fed by you. Don't feed it. When those thoughts come, you must tell yourself, "Stop! Don't go there!" Instead, write down promises in scripture to feed your trust in God.

ANGER WITH GOD

DAY 1—PUTTING A FACE ON GOD

Many counselors, and even pastors, will advise those who are angry with God to forgive Him. However, we know that biblical forgiveness is always in the context of sin, and since God can't sin, He doesn't need forgiveness. But what do we do with our anger, disappointment and hurt that is directed at God? For the next 4 days we will look at reasons we blame God, and on day 5 we will discover a solution to the pain.

The first reason we often blame God is for disciplining our wrongdoing. Consequences are experienced that we don't think we deserve, especially if we have asked for forgiveness.

The foundation of our perception of God is built on how we perceived our parents when we were children. If our parents disciplined us justly, we expect God to discipline us justly. If our parents disciplined us harshly, abusively and unjustly, we expect God to do the same. We may know intellectually that God is a loving God, but because we have put our parents' face on God's face, God's love is often not a reality to us. Let's look at some scriptures to see what God says about His discipline. Read Hebrews 12:7-11.

1. What does it mean when God disciplines us?

2. Why does God discipline us?

3. What does God's discipline produce in us?

4. What does God's face look like to you?

5. What is your attitude towards God's discipline? Is it like Saul's—rebellious and resistant, or is it like David's—broken and contrite?

DAY 2—ACTIONS OF OTHER PEOPLE

The second thing that we often blame God for is the actions of other people. A drunk driver kills a loved one, a wife is raped, or a terrorist hijacks a plane and crashes it into a building. Why doesn't an omnipotent God stop these horrible things from happening?

God gives each of us, including the drunk driver, the rapist, and the terrorist, the choice to love Him. If any of us were forced to love and obey God, it would not be love. We often want the freedom to choose, but resent the fact that God doesn't intervene the way we want Him to. We begin to feel that God is distant, uncaring and even impotent.

When we begin to tell God, "You should have…" or "You could have…" we are humanizing God, making Him into our image instead of us being in His. God is not a man that He should lie. (I Samuel 15:29) He is not human. When you blame God for the action of others, whose face do you put on God?

Let's look at someone in the Bible who put another's face on God. Read Genesis 3:1-13.

1. What choice did God give Adam and Eve in regards to the trees of the garden?

2. Who gave the fruit to Adam?

3. Where was he? (See verse 6)

4. Who ate the fruit?

5. What were the consequences of their decision?

6. Who did Adam blame?

7.   When Adam blamed God for Eve's choices, what did he accuse God of doing?

8.   Read verses 1 and 2. The serpent painted a portrait of God that was contrary to reality. What did that picture look like?

9.   How did that image affect Adam's view of God when confronted with his sin?

10.   What kind of portrait of God has been painted for you?

11.   When you blame God for the actions of others, who does God look like to you?

12.   How does this portrait compare to the one Scripture paints of God?

DAY 3—UNREALISTIC EXPECTATIONS

The next thing that we blame God for involves a set of unrealistic expectations that we all have about life. They go something like this:

- If I am good, nothing bad will happen.
- If something bad happens, I must have done something wrong.
- If I haven't done anything wrong, then God must be wrong for sending something bad.
- Nothing bad will ever happen to those I love. If it does, then God is wrong.

We will examine each expectation and compare it to Scripture. The first fallacy is: If I am good, nothing bad will happen.

For some of us, we have the belief that as long as we are good, trouble will stay far away from us. That belief can be a major motivator in our choices of behavior and lifestyle. While it is true that we reap what we sow, it is also true that bad things do happen to people who do good. Jesus even promised this would happen. Read John 16:33.

1. Does Jesus expect us to have peace?

2. Does Jesus expect us to have troubles?

3. How can we have both?

Now read Matthew 5:45.

4. Who is immune to hardship?

The second fallacy is: If something bad happens, I must have done something wrong. The disciples of Jesus also believed this and, one day, had a theological discussion about it. Read John 9:1-12.

5. From the disciples' point of view, why was this man born blind?

6. From Jesus' point of view, why was he born blind?

7. What work has God displayed in your life through hardship?

8. What miracle are you missing out on because you are focused on the suffering instead of the Savior?

God has the incredible ability to use the hardships in our life for our good (Rom. 8:28). However, so many times we do not see how the bitter things in life added to the sweet can make anything good. Think about the ingredients of a cake. There's flour, sugar, raw eggs, butter, vanilla, and salt. Each of these things by themselves does not taste good (except maybe the sugar). In fact, some of them are quite bitter. But if we leave out any of them, the cake wouldn't be good. The same is true with our lives. God is in the process of baking a cake, and it takes both the bitter and the sweet for the cake to be good.

DAY 4—UNREALISTIC EXPECTATIONS (PART II)

The third fallacy is: If I haven't done anything wrong, then God must be wrong for sending something bad. The best scriptural example of this is Job. Job experienced major tragedy in his life, and his friends told him he must have done something wrong for all this to happen to him. However, Job was a righteous man, so righteous that God bragged about him. Yet, tragedy still struck him. When this happens to us, our tendency is to say that God must be wrong because we didn't do anything to deserve the suffering. Let's see how this fallacy was worked out in Job.

Read Job 1:22, 13:3 and 19:6.

1. What was Job's attitude towards God?

2. How did Job sin in the midst of his suffering?

Read Job 40:1-2 and 8.

3. What was God's response to Job's attitude?

4. How have you condemned God in order to justify yourself?

Read Job 42:1-6.

5. What was Job's response?

6. How have your eyes been opened to a deeper understanding of God as a result of your suffering?

The fourth fallacy is: Nothing bad will ever happen to those I love and nobody that I love will ever die or be hurt. For some of us we can take tragedy upon ourselves, but our anger is incited when we see tragedy we deem undeserved in the life of someone we love. Our child becomes critically ill, a beloved parent suffers with cancer, or a child is left orphaned by a hijacking terrorist. We question, "Why did you let this happen, God? They didn't deserve it. Why didn't You do something?" Two sisters asked those same questions of Jesus. Read John 11:1-42.

7. How did Jesus feel about Mary, Martha and Lazarus?

8. How long did he stay where he was after he heard Lazarus was dying?

9. Did Jesus know what was going to happen?

10. Did Martha blame Jesus for her brother's death?

11. How about Mary?

12. What was Jesus' response to each one?

13. Did the people blame Jesus?

14. Which would have been a greater show of God's power, healing Lazarus or raising him from the dead?

15. What did the people have to do before Jesus raised Lazarus from the dead?

16. What is God asking you to do before He can show His power?

DAY 5—THE SOLUTION

This past week we have looked at the four fallacies or misbeliefs that cause us to be angry with God. Today we will look at solutions for the problem of the negative emotions directed at God. They are:

- Repentance
- Perspective
- Trust/Acceptance
- Allowing for grief

The first solution is found in **repentance**. We can follow Job's example in Job 40:1-5 and 42:4-5. He repented for his belief that God owed him something and his demanding spirit that said, "This is the way life is supposed to be."

1. What have you accused God of that you need to repent of?

The second solution is **perspective**. This has to do with the way we see things, where our focus is. We are like the four blind men trying to identify what is in front of them simply by touch. They each had a different perspective depending on what part of the elephant they were touching. We do not see life the same way that God does because our perspective is limited. Read II Cor. 4:8-9 and 16-18.

2. What does Paul state are light and momentary troubles?

3. How are we renewed day by day?

4. What should we focus on when we experience trials?

5. Where is your focus? Do you need to shift focus? If so, how are you going to start today?

We can keep our focus on the eternal God when we remember the purpose of our trials. Turn to Romans 5:3-5.

6. God uses trials to work good things in us. Write the progression of those things according to Romans.

7. Why should we rejoice in suffering?

8. Why doesn't hope lead to disappointment?

9. How do we know God loves us?

10. Ask Jesus to show you the truth about His love for you.

The third solution is **trust and acceptance**. In C.S. Lewis' book, *The Lion, the Witch, and the Wardrobe*, four children are told that they will meet the great lion Aslan. Fearful of facing the huge beast, they ask if he is a tame lion. Their host laughs at them and tells them that he is not tame, of course, but that he is *good*. This is really a description of God. He is not tame. He cannot be put in a box or commanded to obey us, but He is infinitely good. Let's look at several scriptures to illustrate this point. Read Psalm 37:1-6.

11. What are the benefits of trusting God?

Now read Romans. 9:20-21.

12. Who is the potter? Who is the clay?

13. Think of something that you have created or put together (not your child). Imagine it complaining about where it was put, to whom it was given, and how it was used. What would its accusations or demands be of you?

14. When you complain about your life, what are your accusations or demands of God?

Now read Romans. 8:28.

15. What does God use for good in our lives?

16. For whom does He work all things together for good?

17. What good has come from something you thought was bad?

18. Trust is not a feeling but an action. When we determine to trust God, peace will follow, but it may take time. What do you need to determine to trust God with?

The fourth solution is allowing for grief. This process of grieving often takes time. It also takes work. For those of us who are more stoic, it takes work to face the negative feelings. For those who are very in touch with their emotions, it takes work to take them to the Father. God wants us to grieve. Read John 11:35, Ecclesiastes 3:4, and Psalms 30:5.

19. What losses have you allowed yourself to grieve?

20. What have you lost that you have not grieved?

21. Sometimes we don't grieve because we think we will appear weak and then people won't want to be around us. We don't take the time to grieve but stay busy to avoid the pain. What is keeping you from grieving your losses?

GUILT, SHAME AND SELF-CONDEMNATION

DAY 1—THE GRIP OF GUILT

In today's world, guilt has risen to epidemic proportions. If psychologists and counselors could find a remedy for guilt, more than half their caseload would be healed. One of the prominent methods being taught to reduce guilt is through forgiving one's self. At first, this counsel seems wise and even biblical. However, there are a few difficulties with this theory.

The first problem lies in what we forgive. Review your notes from your introductory session.

1. What do we forgive?

2. What do we not forgive?

We often feel guilty for the sins of other people. A trusted friend molests our child, a parent is abused in a reputable nursing home, our spouse leaves us or has an affair, or we were sexually abused as children. The guilt is compounded when the abuser tells us it is our fault.

Statistics report that 27 percent of women and 16 percent of men have been sexually abused as children.[2] More times than not, their abuser tells them that it is their fault. These precious little children believe the lie and carry their abusers' guilt for decades.

But sometimes we are the ones who have sinned and the guilt becomes unbearable. We had an affair, we had an abortion, or we succumbed to temptation time and time again that resulted in a destructive lifestyle (i.e. overeating, substance abuse, compulsive spending, rage, etc.).

3. What do you feel guilty for?

Can we sin against ourselves? There is one scripture that does allude to sinning against ourselves. Turn to I Corinthians 6:18-20.

4. How can we sin against our body?

5. Who does our body belong to?

6. Why is our body God's temple?

7. Who do we sin against when we sin sexually?

Read James 1:13-14.

8. Why do we sin?

9. What drags us into temptation?

Whenever we are tempted to sin, we are expecting a payoff. There would be no temptation to sin if we didn't expect to get something. Therefore, our sin is not *against* us, but *for* us. Satan is crafty, trying to convince us of a payoff and deceiving us into believing that no one will get hurt in the process. The reality is that there are no victimless sins. My sins affect my husband, my children, my co-workers, everyone with whom I have a relationship. So, then, the problem is not in forgiving ourselves, but in receiving God's forgiveness. Author and counselor Dan Allender says, " Most people don't want to know God's forgiveness because to dance with him requires a level of freedom and sacrifice that is too frightening."

That "dance" was pretty scary for Joseph's brothers who had sold him into slavery and were later at his mercy. After their father's funeral, Joseph's brothers fell at his feet and begged for forgiveness, offering themselves as his slaves. Joseph's reaction was to weep. He was grieved that his brothers would not receive his forgiveness, which had been granted long before. They chose to bind themselves in fear and guilt rather than reveling in the freedom of forgiveness. "Dancing" with God requires cutting off root issues such as works, pride, and misbeliefs. For the next two days, we will study the root issues that keep us from dancing.

DAY 2—CHOPPING DOWN THE TREE—PART I

There are four roots to be cut off. They are:

- Works mentality
- Pride
- Belief that if I have really been forgiven, I won't sin anymore
- Belief that if I ask for forgiveness there will be no consequences

The first root that we will tackle is a **works mentality**. Many of us understand that we cannot work our way into heaven. However, we do feel like we have to work to earn God's love. Many times we use works to reduce our feelings of guilt. This is called penance, using a good action to outweigh a bad one. I yell at my kids, so I take them out for ice cream. I am rude to my co-worker, so I agree to work in her place even when I don't want to. I've done terrible things in my past, so I try to help whomever I can, even if it makes me angry. Taking kids out for ice cream, working in someone's place or helping someone in crisis are all good things. However, when they are used as a means to reduce guilt, we are relying on our own righteousness instead of the blood of Jesus.

Read Is. 64:6.

1. How does God see our righteousness?

Read Philippians 3:4-9.

2. What were Paul's credentials?

3. Why did he count those credentials as loss?

4. If you were writing vs. 4-6, what would you boast about?

5. In what ways do these things hinder your walk with Christ?

6. In whose righteousness does Paul trust? How do you know?

7. In whose righteousness do you trust? How do you know?

The second root to be chopped is a **false pride**. This begins with an unhealthy intro-spection or focus on our sin. It is the belief that our sin is more powerful than God's grace. This results in self-abasement and self-abuse. Before Martin Luther understood grace, he would whip himself and crawl bare-kneed over sharp stones in order to reduce his guilt. We may not do this physically, but we do it emotionally by telling ourselves that we are unacceptable, unworthy and unlovable. Read Romans 8:31-39 to see what God tells us about ourselves.

8. Who justifies us?

9. Who condemns us?

10. What can separate us from God's love?

11. What do you think has separated you from God's love?

12. What do you believe has disqualified you from being used by God?

13. What have you done that made you believe God had stopped loving you?

Having false pride is like saying, "Christ's blood is not sufficient to cover my sin, there-fore, my sin is more powerful than God." It is the belief that we have the power to make Him stop loving us. When we believe that we have the power to make God stop loving us, it is an act of independence from Him. We call this pride because it is the same sin that Adam and Eve succumbed to in their striving to be equal to, or more powerful, than God. Take some time to journal about how works and/or false pride have affected your relationship with God.

DAY 3—CHOPPING DOWN THE TREE—PART II

The third root is the misconception that **if I have really been forgiven, I won't sin anymore**. Guilt often becomes unbearable with habitual sins such as overeating, addictions, anger, etc.

Read about Paul's struggle with sin in Romans 7:15-20.

1.   What does Paul do?

2.   What does he not do?

3.   With what does Paul struggle?

We will always fight against our sinful nature, but there are times that we continue to sin because we have not really considered repentance. A cycle is produced that goes something like this:

- •   I sin.
- •   I feel convicted.
- •   I feel regret or remorse.
- •   I ask for forgiveness for my sin.
- •   I don't change anything in my life.
- •   I find myself in sin again.

The solution does not lie in the need to forgive ourselves but in the need to repent. Repentance means making a 180 degree turn. Think about a clock face. When I am in sin, I am walking in the 12 o'clock position. I may experience regret and turn to the 2 o'clock position but I am still walking in sin. I may then experience remorse and turn to the 4 o'clock position but there is no lasting change. It is only when I turn all the way around to the 6 o'clock position that I have repented. Making that turn is not easy. It may mean going for counseling and/or finding someone to disciple me and/or hold me accountable. It means that I will have to let go of my pride and self-sufficiency by admitting that I need help in this battle. Next, we will find the solution to works, pride, and misbeliefs.

Since we have discovered that self-forgiveness is not the solution to freedom from guilt, we now know that the real problem lies in receiving God's forgiveness. There are several biblical steps to receiving God's forgiveness.

The first step is to **identify the sin**. This step is important when distinguishing between conviction and false guilt. Conviction is an alarm from the Holy Spirit warning us of sin.

False guilt occurs when the enemy or another person accuses us of a sin we have already confessed, or it manifests itself in our feeling responsible for another's sin.

Read II Cor. 7:10-11.

4.   Which type of sorrow is conviction?

5.   Which type of sorrow is false guilt?

6.   What does conviction bring?

7.   What does false guilt bring?

8.   How is a heart changed through conviction?

9.   When have you felt convicted? What was the result?

10.   When have you felt false guilt? What was the result?

Ps. 139:23-24 gives us a good example to pray to distinguish between false guilt and conviction.

11.   What does this prayer ask God to do?

12.   What is God asked to look for?

13.   When He finds it, what is He asked to do?

The everlasting way is God's way; it is the way of obedience. When we sow obedience, we reap the fruit of the Spirit: Love, joy, peace, patience, kindness, goodness, gentleness, faithfulness and self-control. End today by reading John 15:9-11.

DAY 4—FINDING FREEDOM

The second step in the solution to ridding ourselves of guilt is **confession**. This simply means to agree with God that a particular behavior, thought pattern or motivation is not right for you. An example of this is found in II Samuel 24:10, where David says, "I sinned greatly in what I have done. Now, Oh, Lord, I beg You, take away the guilt of your servant. I have done a very foolish thing."

I John 1:9 says, "If we confess our sins, He is faithful and just and will forgive us of our sins and purify us from all unrighteousness." When we confess, God is quick to forgive and remove the sin from our heart. If this is difficult for you to experience, it may be helpful to envision Jesus dying on the cross for that specific sin. If you have been resisting God's forgiveness, you may also need to repent of the works mentality, pride and misbeliefs that have kept you from receiving His grace.

List the things you need to confess.

James 5:16 says, "Therefore, confess your sins to each other and pray for each other so that you might be healed." Either while you are confessing to God or after you have confessed to Him, it may be helpful to confess your sins to another person. This brings accountability and breaks the power of habitual and secret sins. However, don't confess to just anyone. There are certain qualifications for a "confessor":

1. They must be a mature believer who knows how to pray.
2. They must be someone you trust to keep confidentiality, not likely to gossip.
3. They must understand the value of what you are doing.
4. They must be mature enough that they won't be shocked by what you confess.
5. They must be someone who can reflect God's grace and forgiveness.

Write the name of the person you will confess to and the day you intend to do it by.

Name_____   Deadline date _____.

The third step in receiving God's forgiveness is to **remember God's promises**. John White, in his fantasy book *Gaal the Conqueror*, describes false guilt (accusations of already confessed sin) in his story of two Canadian children transported to another world. Gaal, the Christ figure, had given John and Eleanor a mission with specific instructions. They disobeyed Gaal's instructions and end up trapped in an iron cage. After suffering in their imprisonment, they ask for forgiveness and Gaal explains the cage. "Once you've been caught in a cage of this sort (it's called a guilt cage—you can sometimes get trapped in it even when you haven't disobeyed instructions) what you do is remember that I have set you free—free from all guilt cages."

Once you have identified and confessed your sin, you may still find yourself in a guilt cage. The iron bars look and feel real, but are only illusions. John and Eleanor found themselves in that very situation, but were able to walk through the bars by having faith in what Gaal had told them. "I have set you free." The bars that imprison you can be walked through by having faith in God's promises. There are hundreds of promises in the Bible concerning forgiveness—here are a few:

1. **Romans 8:1**—God no longer condemns us.
2. **II Corinthians 5:19**—God does not count our sins against us.
3. **Lamentations 3:22-23**—God's mercies are new every morning.

Search the scripture or use the above to find promise verses of God's forgiveness for your sin. What are your promise verses?

The fourth step is to be prepared for accusations coming from the enemy. Satan's job description is to be your prosecuting attorney. He wants to keep us in that "guilt cage" and we need to be prepared for his tactics. Revelation 12:11 says that we can overcome Satan by the blood of the Lamb and the word of our testimony. A testimony is simply a report of what has happened or what you experienced. Write your testimony of God's forgiveness. In this testimony include the specific sin for which Satan will accuse you, as well as scripture that speaks of God's grace and Christ's righteousness. Then praise God for what He has done for you.

Believing that we can forgive ourselves implies that we are the judge, that we are on the throne. A believer in Jesus Christ has the Lord sitting on the throne of his heart and, therefore, only He has the right to forgive us. Go to Him to seek forgiveness and experience Him as the Prince of Peace.

DAY 5—CHOPPING ROOT #4

The fourth root to be sacrificed is the belief that **if I ask for forgiveness there will be no consequences**. David did not believe this lie from the enemy. In fact, there were times when God convicted David of sin, David repented and then God even gave him a choice about the consequence. Let's look at one of those instances in I Chronicles 21:1-17.

1. Of what sin did David repent?

2. What was God's response?

3. What were the three choices of consequences?

4. What choice did David make and why?

5. How did David's sin affect the people?

6. What did David learn from the consequences of his sin?

Our God is a good Daddy. He disciplines His own because He loves us. However, knowing that it is done out of love does not make it fun to endure. Look at Hebrews 12:11.

7. Is discipline pleasant or painful?

8. What does it produce?

Even if we know in our heads that discipline is good for us, it doesn't exempt us from the grieving that follows. When we experience consequences, it is often in the form of losing things that are dear to us. We lose our innocence, trust, reputation, and pride (but that's a good loss, even though it hurts). We even lose the promised payoff of sin. Grief and guilt are similar feelings and sometimes we mistake the two. We think we are feeling guilty when we are actually grieving our losses.

This often happens in the case of childhood sexual abuse and rape. The victim has done nothing wrong, but ends up feeling ashamed and guilty for the sins committed against them. To make matters worse, the perpetrator often tells the victim that it was all her fault. This is especially damaging if the victim is a child. If you have been a victim of sexual abuse, **"It is not your fault!"** What you are feeling is the grief of losing all the things that were stolen from you by that horrendous act. Tamar felt the same feelings when her half-brother raped her. Read her reaction in II Samuel 13:18-20.

9. Why did Tamar tear the ornamental robes?

10. Why did she put ashes on her head?

11. How did Tamar spend the rest of her life?

Tamar never finished grieving. She never allowed God to enter that wounded place in her heart so He could bind up her wound and heal her heart. Turn to Isaiah 61:1-3.

12. What has Jesus been sent to do?

13. What will He give instead of ashes?

14. What will He give to replace a spirit of despair?

15. What have you been grieving that you previously thought was guilt?

STEP 2—SEEKING GOD'S FORGIVENESS

DAY 1—IT TAKES TWO TO TANGO

Last week our focus was on the wrongs that we know we have done. This week we will focus on some areas we may have never thought of before in relationship to our offender.

When we think of the offenses done against us, often the focus is on the offender's behavior with very little focus on our own. Our eyes are blinded to our own part in the matter and we end up playing the blame game. The reality is that it takes two to tango and often we have been dancing right along with our offender. Some of you may be thinking, "Not me! I didn't do anything wrong."

Research has shown that even in domestic violence there is a dance done by both parties. She pushes his buttons, he pushes hers and neither knows how to stop until it becomes physical.

The only offense I know where there is not a dance is in childhood sexual abuse or rape. The victim is never at fault. If you fall into this category, however, don't skip this chapter. You will find many things in this chapter that will apply to you in the following days.

Let's look at a couple who excelled at the blame game. Read Genesis 3:1-13. Two weeks ago we looked at this passage from the perspective of Adam blaming God. But Adam also blamed another.

1. How did Eve get the fruit?

2. Was she forced to eat the fruit?

3. Did the serpent cause Eve to sin?

4. How did Adam get the fruit?

5.   Was he forced to eat the fruit?

6.   Did Eve cause Adam to sin?

7.   Who did Adam blame for his sin?

8.   Who did Eve blame for her sin?

We can clearly see from this text that each party was responsible for his/her own sin. Each had the opportunity to say, "No, I'm not going to do that." Neither took responsibility. Our ancient ancestors taught us well, and we continue to dance the same dance.

For the next two days we will look at our own waltz. Take some time now to pray that God will allow you to see the steps your feet have taken in your dance with your offender.

DAY 2—MAY I HAVE THIS DANCE?

Today and tomorrow we will look at our own part in the offending event. This is a difficult step in the process of forgiveness because self-righteousness has become a protective wall for many. We have erased the memory of our own actions so we can justify the anger and unforgiveness toward our offender.

Today we will focus on the dance during the offending event. The first scenario we will address is one in which you were the initial sinner. Sometimes we screw up and hurt someone and the retaliation is much greater than we think we deserve. We then focus on our hurt instead of on our sin.

The second scenario is when the other person sinned first, but you finished the fight. As a child on the playground, a little boy called me "skinny." That hurt my feelings so I called him "fatty." My intention was to hurt him as much as he had hurt me. That was a wrong reaction and it was sinful. Jesus taught about this in the Sermon on the Mount, but first let's read Leviticus 24:19-20.

1.   What is the punishment for someone who injures another?

2.   What is the focus of the passage?

During the time of Jesus there was debate between the Pharisees concerning this passage. One leader said that it should be taken literally, the other believed that it was just a guide for equal retaliation to prevent feuds from happening. Read Matthew 5:38-42 to find what Jesus taught.

3.   How was Jesus' teaching different from the Leviticus passage?

People come to me who are in difficult relationships. I counsel them to not retaliate, but to respond with love. Often they retort that it is too difficult, that the offender deserves a negative response, or that it is not fair because the other person will think that it is okay to behave in that way. All of those things may be true, but it is not the way of the cross. It is impossible to respond to hurt in love without the power of the Holy Spirit and without keeping the focus on Jesus and off of the other person.

Go back through your journal, look at the list of offenses and note when you either started the dance or finished the job. This exercise is not meant to invalidate your hurt. Just because you started the fight or had a sinful reaction to another's sin does not let the other person off the hook. What this exercise will do is give you a reality check into the truth, for it is the truth that sets you free.

DAY 3—BUILDING WALLS OF PROTECTION

Yesterday we looked at the tango that can happen when someone sins against us. We examined instances when we started the dance and when we finished it. But not every incident falls in either of those categories. Sometimes we don't react in the heat of it all, especially as children. However, what does occur is a reaction that becomes a lifestyle behavior of sin. These are known in the psychological world as "defense mechanisms." These are patterns of relating to people that are meant to protect us from further hurt. Some examples of these are manipulation, control, passive-aggression, obesity, withdrawal, codependency, enabling, etc. Other means of protecting ourselves is through addictions, meaning we use a person or substance to dull our pain. This is not just a modern-day problem but an age-old one.

In Deuteronomy 28, God tells the nation of Israel the blessings that will come through obedience and the curses that will come from disobedience. The blessings listed include provision, fertility and safety from enemies. The curses include famine, futility and war. Read Deuteronomy 28:49-52.

1.   Describe the nation that will come against a disobedient Israel.

2.   What will they leave Israel?

3.   In what will a disobedient Israel trust?

4.   What is the result of trusting in walls for protection?

5.   Why would God want their "protection" to crumble?

Read Psalms 20:7, 44:6-8 and 49:5-15.

6.   According to these passages what are some choices in which to place trust?

7.   In Psalm 49 the psalmist describes someone whose trust for protection is in himself. What are the different ways he describes one trusting in self?

8.   What is the result of trusting in self?

9.   What/who was the Psalmist's choice for trust?

For many, this concept of trusting someone or something other than God for protection is an eye-opener. Either you did not realize that you were doing that or you did not know that it was unhealthy. We all use defense mechanisms but are often unaware of what we are doing and the devastating effects they have on ourselves and those around us. Take a few moments to pray and ask the Lord to reveal who/what you have been trusting in to protect you from harm, and what has been the result. Then list those people or things and the harm that has come from misplaced trust. An example is given for you in the exercise on the next page.

Things you have trusted in:	Consequences of that trust:
Controlling others	Devalues others, manipulates others, etc.
_____	_____
_____	_____
_____	_____
_____	_____
_____	_____

DAY 4—PEDESTALS AND PITS

A TALE OF TWO WOMEN

Several years ago, I counseled two women going through similar situations. Both were stay-at-home moms, who had great respect for their husbands and thought their marriages were normal. Both were shocked and surprised to find their husbands had committed adultery. They both attended one of my forgiveness groups, and when we came to this chapter their reactions were very different.

Rosemary actually walked out of the group because she could not believe that she had contributed in any way to the infidelity. Linda was in the depths of despair believing that the infidelity was totally her fault. They were both right and they were both wrong. Rosemary had placed herself on a pedestal of self-righteousness. It was true that she did not push him into the arms of another, however, she played a part in the circumstances that made it easier for him to give in to the temptation. For instance, Rosemary ran the roost. She did not believe that her husband was capable and let him know that. Therefore, it was easy for her husband to become involved with someone who would give him the encouragement and acceptance that he craved.

Linda, on the other hand, was a chameleon. So hungry for acceptance, she would become whoever her husband wanted her to be. If he said she was too weak, she would pool her efforts to become strong. If he said she should be more spiritual, she would get up an hour earlier for a quiet time. Whatever he wanted, she gave. She worshipped the ground he walked on. He became her god. But being her god was too heavy a load to bear, so he looked for a lighter load. Rather than ending up on a pedestal, Linda was in a pit of despair. She believed that if she had done more, or better, she would have saved her marriage. But the saving of a marriage takes two willing parties and he was simply unwilling.

Both women are examples of typical reactions to this chapter. The purpose of this chapter is not to condemn or to invalidate the hurt. The purpose of this chapter is to remind us that we are on the same level as our offender. In God's eyes, there are no pedestals or pits. It is a level playing field.

Read Jeremiah 17:9.

1.   How does God describe man's heart?

Now go to Romans 3:9-24.

2.   Who is righteous (right unto or by themselves)?

3.   Who does good of their own accord?

4.   What is the purpose of the law?

5.   How do we obtain righteousness?

6.   Can your offender obtain righteousness? If so, how?

7.   You are someone else's offender. Who have you offended either through starting the dance, finishing the dance, or by a lifestyle behavior?

DAY 5—CHANGING THE DANCE

The last three days have been emotional wringers. Not wanting to leave this chapter on a negative note, a solution is needed to change the dance. It's a simple solution, but often difficult to carry out.

The first step is to **confess our sin** whether it was the start, finish or continuation of the dance. I John 1:9 says that when we confess our sins, our relationship with God is restored. This is the easy part because we know that God is gracious, understanding and compassionate.

The second step is more difficult. It involves **confessing our sin to the ones we have offended**. Sometimes it's scary to confess our part in the dance because we fear that our offenders will then believe that they are justified in their actions. This step goes against our very nature and our culture. We need to go a step further as well. We need to confess to those who have been damaged by our walls of protection. This may include spouses, children, friends, co-workers, parents, siblings, fellow church members, etc. James 5:16 says that when we confess our sin, it brings healing which may result in the softening of the other person's heart.

The third step is to **ask those specific people for forgiveness**. Just saying, "I'm sorry" is not enough. Asking, "Will you forgive me," is taking responsibility for the behavior, and communicating that forgiveness is needed. Asking the question also requires a response, whereas saying, "I'm sorry" does not.

The final step is to **praise and thank God for His forgiveness**, cleansing you from sin, and clothing you in righteousness.

So, your task for today is to list in your journal the people whom you have sinned against, and what the specific sin was. Then confess the sin to God, asking for forgiveness. Finally, set a date for confessing to that person(s) via mail, e-mail, telephone or in person. If the person is deceased or you do not know how to reach them, then confessing your sin to God is sufficient.

Note: The practice of building walls is one that is deeply ingrained. It will take more than the above to tear down many of those walls. There are lots of resources that will help in this process. Counselors, seminars, books and videos are available to assist you in tearing down the walls. A sample list of resources is provided in the Appendix. There are many more available that are not listed.

STEP 3—BECOMING OTHER-CENTERED

DAY 1—CHANGING OUR GAZE

For the majority of this Bible study we have looked inward, analyzing our hearts and minds, our hurts and woundedness. This has been a good thing, especially for those who like to avoid introspection. However, it is time to begin focusing on others, looking beyond our own hurts into the hurts of those around us. This gets us out of the victim mentality, which can cause us to shift blame, be a martyr, focus on what we don't have and rehash the pain over and over and over again. When we are out of the victim mentality, we accept responsibility for our own behavior and not for another's. Also, we develop an attitude of gratitude and can trust God with our pain. For our scripture today we will look at One who is truly other-centered. Read Philippians 2:1-11

1.   What attitude is Paul requesting from the Philippians?

2.   How does he tell them to achieve that?

3.   What "rights" did Jesus give up to become the human Messiah?

4.   What were the rewards of giving up those "rights"?

5.   What "rights" will you have to give up in order to forgive your offender?

6.   What does it mean to be like-minded? (same word in v.2 as v.5)

7.   What does humility mean? (lowliness of mind, heart or thought)

8.   What is the difference between humility and low self-esteem?

9.   Co-dependent is often the label given to those who give up their rights. A definition of co-dependency is when one lays aside their wants, needs or interests in order to gain the acceptance, love or affirmation from another human being. How is this passage different from co-dependency?

10. What does it mean to "consider others better than yourselves"?

11. How do you get encouragement, comfort, fellowship, tenderness and compassion?

12. What do you base your self-esteem on?

13. How do you have unity with others who are different from yourself?

DAY 2—A STORY OF SELFISHNESS

Our society is a breeding ground for the dangerous disease of selfishness. We are constantly told "believe in yourself," "if it feels good do it," "take care of number one," "you can have it now," "you can have it all." With this brainwashing, our deceitful heart makes us believe that we are the center of the universe. This is not a new phenomenon. Jonah suffered from the same disease on a larger scale. He thought that his nation was the only one loved by God, and the only one that should be loved by God. Take a few moments and read the book of Jonah.

1.   What did God tell Jonah to do?

2.   Why didn't Jonah want to go to Ninevah? (Chap. 4:2)

3.   Where was Jonah's focus?

4.   Why do you not want God to be compassionate to your offender?

5.   Why did Jonah believe that he had a right to be angry?

6.   Why do you believe you have a right to be angry with your offender?

Jonah felt that he had a right to be angry because (1) the Ninevites were wicked people who had slaughtered his fellow countrymen, and (2) Israel was the chosen nation, not Ninevah. Why should God be merciful to them? We are often just like Jonah. We know the wickedness of our offenders and we fear that if we forgive, God will let them off the hook. We as believers are also the chosen ones of God and we wonder why God wants to be merciful to our offenders. These two issues reveal a lack of trust in God's justice and a lack of appreciation of God's grace.

God is a just God. Even though He was merciful in the book of Jonah, 150 years later Ninevah had forgotten their conviction and God's grace. The book of Nahum is the prophecy against Ninevah, which was destroyed, never to be rebuilt again. We often don't see the consequences that our offender reaps. We do not know the pain in their heart. We need to trust that God's justice is as great as His mercy. If this day's work has been difficult for you, go back and review Week 4. Tomorrow we will look at the grace of God and begin practicing living in that grace.

DAY 3—AN UNCONDITIONAL LOVE STORY (PART 1)

Today we will read a different kind of love story. Hosea is the story of a prophet who was instructed by God to marry a prostitute. In the Old Testament, the events in the lives of prophets were used as pictures to communicate God's truth or His heart to His people. The love story in Hosea parallels the love story between God and His bride Israel. Read Hosea 1-3:2

1. Who did God tell Hosea to marry and what was she like? (1:2-3)

2. Who were Gomer's children?

    Her firstborn was _____ (1:4) which means "scattered."
    Her daughter was _____ (1:6) which means "not loved."
    Her third child was _____ (1:9) which means "not my people."

3. What is the vilest adultery? (1:2)

4. Why did Gomer go to other lovers? (2:5)

5. Where do you go to get your supply of comfort, security, love, affirmation, and provision?

6. What is God's response to Gomer? (2:6-7, 14, 16, 17, 21-23 & 3:1-2)

7. Take five minutes and list as many blessings as you can think of in your life.

8. Which ones have you taken for granted?

9. Which have you attributed to yourself or other sources instead of God?

10. Which have you specifically used to honor God?

11. What blessings do you "spend" to get your comfort, security, love, affirmation, and provision?

DAY 4—AN UNCONDITIONAL LOVE STORY (PART 2)

Yesterday we read of the parallel between Israel's sin of idolatry, and Gomer's sin of adultery. The point God is making is that we are all Gomers. We have all run after "idols" to satisfy the hunger of our hearts. Today we will continue the story as God relates His heart to Israel. Read Hosea 10-14.

1.   What happens when we rely on our own strength? (10:13-14)

2.   Look back over your life and ask God to show you how He loved you as a child; taught you to walk; led you with cords of human kindness and with ties of love, and how He healed you and fed you. (11:1-4)

Read II Timothy 2:13 and Hosea 11:7-11.

3.   What does this show you about God's character?

4.   What does God desire most for us? (13:4)

5.   What can we do to keep from getting proud? (13:6)

6.   Make a list of the things God has freed you from.

7.   Make a list of the things for which God has forgiven you.

8.   How does God respond to our repentance? (14:4)

As God extended His grace to Gomer, He extends it to us. His mercies are new to us every morning. He never tires of extending His forgiveness, even to our offenders. Just as we need to remember that every one of us are Gomers and God has compassion for us in our sin, our offenders are also Gomers and God has that same compassion for them. However, let's not live as the prostitute Gomer, but as the Gomer who has been restored and blessed and honored by her Beloved Husband.

DAY 5—HEART CHECK

It's time for a checkup on where you are in the forgiveness process. On a scale of 1 to 10 how closely does your heart match the verses that follow, 1 being "My heart feels the exact opposite of this verse," 5 being "I wrestle back and forth," and 10 being "My heart is totally in line with this verse."

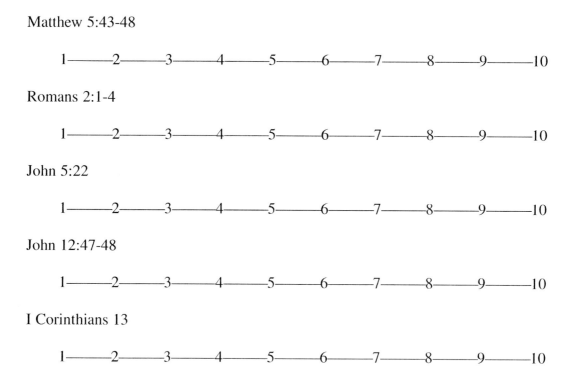

Matthew 5:43-48

1———2———3———4———5———6———7———8———9———10

Romans 2:1-4

1———2———3———4———5———6———7———8———9———10

John 5:22

1———2———3———4———5———6———7———8———9———10

John 12:47-48

1———2———3———4———5———6———7———8———9———10

I Corinthians 13

1———2———3———4———5———6———7———8———9———10

The bottom line question is "Do I love my enemy?" If the answer is no, check your heart against these statements:

1. **I still feel I have a right to be angry.** Go back to Week 1 and Week 4.

2. **I don't trust God's justice.** Go back to Week 5.

3. **My enemy is totally at fault.** Go back to Week 7.

4. **I'm afraid I will be vulnerable to hurt if I love my enemies.** Review Week 2 & 3.

5. **I don't believe my enemy deserves the same compassion as I do.** Go back to days 3 and 4 of this week.

STEP 4—FORSAKING REVENGE

DAY 1—VENGEANCE IS MINE

The fourth step in the forgiveness process is forsaking revenge. This means giving up revenge to leave room for the wrath or judgment of God. We take revenge in many different ways: the silent treatment; guilt-heaping; or verbal or physical assault. We can bring up stuff from the past that we've said we've forgiven but really haven't because it's still there in times of anger. We can gossip. Sometimes revenge can be so subtle we are unaware of it ourselves. Revenge qualifies as anything we do to punish our offender or make our offender "pay." Read Deuteronomy 32:35 & 43.

1.   Whose job is it to avenge (punish or judge)?

2.   When will God take vengeance?

3.   On whom does God take vengeance? (v. 43)

4.   What/who does He make atonement for?

The people who offended us are God's responsibility, not ours. Read Proverbs 20:22

5.   For whom are we to wait?

6.   What will He do?

Now read Romans 12:19-21.

7.   How do we leave room for God's wrath?

Leaving room for God's wrath requires us to step out of the way. I can think of two possible reasons why He may want us to step out of the way. One reason may be to warn us so that we will not get hurt in the process of His vengeance. The other possibility is that He will stay His hand to let us see how ineffective we are in our vengeance. We are not God and He will let us continue in our impotence to remind us of that fact.

8.   What does "heap burning coals on his head" mean?

I have found 3 different interpretations to this phrase. One is that it is a "horrible punishment reserved for the wicked."[4] Another interpretation is that wearing a pot of burning coals on the head was an Egyptian sign of repentance.[5] However, in this context it is more likely that the phrase refers to a kindness done that may initially hurt but then bring repentance. In other words, "by conferring a favor on your enemy, you recall the wrong he has done to you, so that he repents, with pain of heart.[6] This favor should be done without verbally reminding the offender so as to not be manipulating guilt and condemnation resulting in revenge.

9.   What does seeking revenge do to you? How does revenge overcome you?

DAY 2—RIGHTEOUS ANGER VS. REVENGE (PART I)

There is a place for righteous anger because without it our love is impotent and passionless. The opposite of love is not hatred; the opposite of love is indifference. When we hate someone, there is a passion that is involved. With love there is passion; but with indifference there isn't. There is no feeling, just apathy.

But how do you know the difference between righteous anger and what the Bible calls "man's anger"? There are several characteristics of righteous anger that can serve as a checklist. Look at the following characteristics and match them to the appropriate scriptures.

Righteous anger leaves room for restoration.	Romans 12:19
Righteous anger gets out of God's way.	Luke 6:27-31
Righteous anger involves love.	James 1:19-20
Righteous anger involves mercy.	Hosea 1-3
Righteous anger comes slowly and ends quickly.	Romans 12:21

Revenge tends to progress to the Hatfields and McCoys or the Serbs and Albanians. It never ends, the payback is never enough, and there is always justification for more revenge.

Revenge gets in the way of God. The avenger gets in the line of fire. God, not wanting to hit the wrong one, will withhold the judgment until He has a clear shot. So when we step out of the way and bless, love and show mercy to our enemy, God can then do His work (which gets much better results).

Check your anger against the above list to see how righteous it is. Tomorrow we will discuss the last characteristic of righteous anger.

DAY 3—RIGHTEOUS ANGER VS. REVENGE (PART II)

Yesterday we listed several characteristics of righteous anger. Today we will address the final characteristic: Righteous anger prevents evil, it does not promote evil. Yesterday we saw how God calls us to act towards our offender, with love and mercy. But sometimes God calls us to act in some not so "loving" ways. We will look at three examples of anger in Scripture and see which is righteous and which is not. Read Exodus 32:1-4, 19-35.

1. What were the people doing while Moses was on the mountain with God?

2. What was the first thing Moses saw when he came down from the mountain?

3. What did Moses do?

4. What was the result of his actions?

Now read Numbers 20:2-12.

5. What did the people do?

6. What did Moses do?

7. Why did he strike the rock?

8. Think back to the five steps of resolving anger (Week 4). What did striking the rock reveal about Moses' relationship with God?

9. What change did it bring to the people?

10. What was the result of striking the rock?

Here are two examples of Moses' anger. One was righteous, the other was not. Maybe the difference is whom Moses was fighting for. When he broke the tablets, he was angry that the people had become idol worshipers. His anger was in line with God's. He knew it was God's battle and that he was fighting with Him. When he was angry with the people for complaining about the lack of water, he took it as a personal affront. He forgot that it wasn't about him, but about God, and consequently started his own battle. To let this sink in a little deeper, let's look at Mark 11:15-19.

11. Why did Jesus drive the animals, merchants, and buyers out of the temple area?

12. Where were the merchants selling?

This particular area was set aside for Gentiles who had converted to Judaism to worship. They could not go anywhere else in the temple.

13. Who is God's house for?

14. What was the result of Jesus' actions?

One result was that the Gentiles' place of worship was returned to them. The temple once again became a house of prayer for all nations. Secondly, Jesus' actions incited the priests to find a way to kill Him. A third result was that the temple was purified for the Final Sacrifice; Jesus was crucified 4 days later.

15. Who was Jesus fighting for?

16. Who are you fighting for? How do you know?

DAY 4—A GOOD EXAMPLE

God is so good to give us real life examples in the Bible. There are very few superheroes in Scripture because the people are exactly like us. There is a really good example of an ordinary guy who has just made some changes in the kingdom and now his enemies are rising up against him. Read about Jehosephat in II Chronicles 20:1-30.

1. Who came to make war on Judah?

2. What did Jehosephat do when he heard the news?

3. What right did these nations have to make war on Judah?

4. On whose power did Jehosephat rely?

5. Where are his eyes fixed?

6. Why does God tell them not to be afraid?

7. Who will fight the battle?

8. Who's fighting your battle?

9. Why are you afraid to let God handle your battle?

10. How did Judah approach the battleground?

11. How did God deliver them?

12. What was their reward? (vs. 25, 29-30)

God does reward us when we trust in Him. God rewarded Judah's trust so much that it took them three days to gather the plunder. But the greatest reward that Judah received was peace and rest on every side. That is what God will give you when you let Him fight your battles.

DAY 5—PRACTICAL APPLICATION

1. **Change our focus**—If any of us had been in Jehosephat's shoes, it would have been very easy for us to fix our eyes on our enemies and on the potential damage they could do. Our eyes would also be fixed on protecting ourselves by searching for weapons or defenses. Somehow Jehosephat was able to tear his gaze off of the circumstances around him and fix his eyes on his only true Salvation. The struggle in forsaking revenge is in taking our eyes off the one who has wounded us and fixing our gaze on the Healer. We're so afraid that if we change our focus, someone will sneak up from behind and wound us again. But God calls us to trust in His faithful protection and deliverance. Moses changed his focus from the Lord to the stick in his hand and God called him on his idolatry. When we focus on our enemies, our circumstances or our self-protection, we are worshipping those things. When we fix our eyes on Jesus, despite the potential dangers around us, that is true worship. Journal about what has been your focus and how it needs to change.

2. **Remember who's the judge**—It's God's job to bring judgment because He does it so much better than we do. Our purpose in wanting revenge is that we really, at a heart of hearts level, want repentance. We think that if we just punish them enough and cause them enough pain, that they will repent. But we do not know their heart as God knows their heart. God knows exactly what will bring about repentance. In your journal, list ways you have taken revenge and repent of them.

3. **Trust God for His justice**—Forsaking revenge involves trusting God. It is His battle not ours. He calls us, just as He called Jehosephat, to "stand firm and see the deliverance of the Lord." In Ephesians 6, He tells us to do the same thing with regard to spiritual warfare. After we have done all He has commanded, we are to "stand firm." God often directs us to do things in regards to our offender, but not to *fight the battle*. Take time to journal about your battles and give them to the Lord for Him to fight. He is big enough to handle all of them at the same time.

4. **Check out your anger**—It's very easy for us to justify our anger by labeling it as righteous. But, as we've seen from Days 2 and 3 of this week's study, there is a major difference between man's anger and righteous anger. When forsaking revenge, check your anger against the characteristics of righteous anger. If they line up, that's a good indication that you are offended because the Lord has been offended. If your anger does not line up, then go back to Week 4, Day 5, and go through the steps of resolving anger.

Finally, forsaking revenge is a matter of the will. It's a choice that I make. It has nothing to do with my feelings. I don't have to feel like giving up revenge; but I do have to choose to give it up.

STEP 5—DESIRING RESTORATION

DAY 1—LOOKING THROUGH GOD'S GLASSES

The fifth step in the forgiveness process is **desiring restoration**—first between the offender and God, and then between the offender and myself. This involves separating the *person* from the *behavior* by viewing the person from God's perfect perspective and not our wounded perspective.

Read Psalm 139:1-16. Put your offender's name wherever this passage uses the words me, I or my.

1. What does the Lord know about your offender?

2. Where is God in relationship to your offender?

3. How did God create your offender?

4. How far in advance did God plan for your offender?

5. How does this change your perspective of your offender?

DAY 2—DOOR A OR DOOR B?

The second thing that we need to do when desiring restoration is to imagine what our offender would be like if he or she was repentant and totally restored to God and man. Using the concept of choosing Door A and Door B like they used to do on the game shows, which one would you choose? If Door A were the person in total pain with lots of judgment upon their head, would we choose Door A? Or would we choose Door B, which is the repentant person, exactly who God created them to be and in a right relationship with God. Which door would we choose? Do we want the door of this person's life full of pain, or do we want the door of this person's life revealing restoration with God?

We do not know the plans God has for people or how He intends to use them, but He does. Think about the men Jesus chose as His disciples. Let's look at a few of them, where He found them and what became of them. Read Matthew 9:9-13.

1. What was Matthew's profession?

2. How did the Jews feel about tax collectors?

Jews considered Jewish tax collectors to be traitors because they helped the Romans to find Jews who owed taxes. They often charged more than Rome required and pocketed the difference. The Jewish tax collector was like a slave adding burdens to his brother in order to benefit from the master.

3. How do you think the other disciples felt about having a "traitor" on their team?

4. What became of Matthew? (Hint: Who wrote this book of the Bible?)

Now read Luke 22:54-62

5. How many times did Peter deny Jesus?

6. When Peter denied Jesus the third time, what did Jesus do?

7. How do you think Jesus felt?

8.   What did Peter do after he saw Jesus looking at him?

9.   Did Jesus get to see his grief?

Read Acts 11:1-18 to see what became of Peter.

10.   What was Peter told to do by the Spirit?

11.   What was the result?

12.   How fervently did Peter defend his actions and beliefs?

13.   Where would you be spiritually if Peter had not preached to the Gentiles?

There are many other examples of Jesus' earthly friends who were found in bad situations or who betrayed him in some way. Jesus took risks in choosing these men, but he had a different perspective. He saw who they would become *before* any evidence of change occurred. God can grant you that gift if you really want it. Ask Jesus to let you see through His eyes to comprehend the potential of your offender.

DAY 3—WHY DO WE WANT CHANGE?

Yesterday we learned that Jesus saw change in a person before there was any outward evidence that change had occurred. Part of forgiveness is wanting change in our offender, but it can also be part of revenge. Much of revenge is motivated by our desire to change our offender. The difference in wanting change in forgiveness and wanting change in revenge is in *our motivation* for wanting change.

A forgiving heart desires change for the person's sake, not for personal enjoyment of the outcome or to benefit from it (i.e. protection from future hurt, etc.). The reality is that we may never see this person become restored to the Lord. They may move away. We may move away. Our paths may not cross again. But do I still desire restoration? Do I still pray for them to come back to the Lord? Even if they're going to church, reading their Bible, and doing "spiritual" things, and there's still this sin that has affected me that they're not repentant of, do I still pray that God will reveal it to them so that their relationship will become even closer to the Lord? Do I want change for their sake, or do I want change for my sake? I need to sacrifice the desire to see the change.

Jesus had to give up the hope of change in one of his disciples, Judas. Read the following passages about Judas: Mark. 3:13-19, John 12:4-6, and Mark 14:17-21.

1. When did Jesus "discover" that Judas would betray him?

2. Did Jesus know that Judas was stealing money from him?

3. Did Jesus know the motivation for Judas wanting to sell the perfume?

4. Jesus predicted Judas' betrayal in Mark 14, did Jesus treat him any differently?

5. Did the disciples know by Jesus' behavior who would betray him?

6. Did Jesus love him any less?

I don't think that any of us have been betrayed the way Jesus was by Judas. His betrayal brought Jesus to the most painful and shameful death experience in that time. Yet Jesus continued to show love and compassion to Judas throughout the entire ordeal. This is true forgiveness; Jesus was never rewarded by change in His offender.

DAY 4—O, PROTECTOR OF MY SOUL

There are many motivations for wanting our offender to change. Oftentimes we want change for our own sake so that we won't be hurt any more. We need to trust God, not people, for our hearts. This leads us to the fourth characteristic in desiring restoration. It involves yielding our hearts to God for His protection and strength. As we talked about in Step 2, are we putting our trust in our own defense mechanisms? Are we putting our trust in the emotional walls we put around ourselves for protection from hurt? Or are we putting our trust in God to protect our hearts? He is the protector of our souls. When we want to protect ourselves, God will say, "Have at it. I'm going to show you how fallible those walls are. You will find out those walls will not keep the enemy out. I'm going to show you that instead, they keep you trapped inside." So we need to begin to tear down those walls and trust in God as our protector to keep the enemy out. Even when we experience hurt, God will be faithful to heal that wound.

Let's see how one of God's prophets lived this out in II Kings 6:8-23.

1. Why was Elisha not afraid of his enemy?

2. Who rescued Elisha?

3. Where can you find refuge?

4. Do you have to run away?

Now read Psalm 11.

5. Where is the Lord?

6. What is He doing?

7. What does the Lord hate?

8. What does He love?

Now read Psalm 7:14-16

9. What happens when we take matters into our own hands?

DAY 5—GOD'S DESIRE

Our God is complex. He can not be dissected and analyzed. Yet we can learn much from looking at the complexity of His character and attempting to understand it so that we may become more like Him.

I have found that the biggest hindrance to forgiveness is a misunderstanding of how God deals with people. We tend to believe lies such as, "If I forgive, God will just let them off the hook and they will never pay" or "If I forgive, they won't know it was wrong or how much it hurt." There are many variations on this theme and yours may sound slightly different. How do you think God feels about people who choose destruction over obedience? Look at the following verses and match the responses.

1. Psalms 37:13		a.	Saves the lost
2. Romans. 5:8		b.	Will not allow to enter heaven
3. Matthew 7:22-23		c.	Resists the proud
4. Matthew 11:20-24		d.	Doesn't want any to perish
5. 2 Peter 3:9		e.	Laughs at the wicked
6. James 4:6		f.	Pleased when the wicked repent
7. Luke 19:10		g.	Will punish
8. Luke 17:1-2		h.	Will judge harshly
9. Ezekiel. 33:11		i.	Takes no pleasure in the death of the wicked
10. Ezekiel 18:21-23		j.	Died for sinners

How does God experience all these opposing emotions at the same time? The key is that He is God and I am not. Often I limit God to my human experiences and abilities. He can look at a person and feel love, hatred, mercy and justice all at the same time. Our challenge is to trust in His goodness, fairness, justice and mercy, leaving our offender in His hands and doing everything in our power to be at peace with that person.

HEART CHECKS

1. When we don't desire restoration, we are really no better than the one who has offended us, and we need to go back to Step 2.

2. Do I pray for God's blessing for my offender and rejoice when it comes, remembering it is God's kindness that leads to repentance?

STEP 6 PART I— CONFRONTING THE BELIEVER

The last step of forgiveness is confrontation. **Confrontation is motivating the offender towards repentance.** The goal is not to demand repentance, but to provide the *opportunity* for repentance. If my goal is repentance, I will be disappointed. But if my goal is to provide the opportunity for repentance, then when I confront, I will never be disappointed because I have done what I needed to do to accomplish my goal. Whether they repent or not is their responsibility, not mine.

Confronting a believer is different from confronting an unbeliever. The rules are not the same. This chapter will focus on confrontation in general and confronting the believer in specific.

DAY 1—PREPARATION FOR CONFRONTATION

Before we confront, we need to be sure that our heart is pure and right. We can have as many reasons for wanting to avoid confrontation as we can have for being eager for confrontation. Below are several reasons we may look forward to confrontation. Let's examine what the Bible says about those motives and what to do with them.

VENTING EMOTIONS

Sometimes we want to confront in order to release our pent up emotions and give ourselves a cathartic explosion. We feel better afterward but the target is left verbally and emotionally bloody from the whole ordeal. Fill in the blanks for Proverbs 12:18.

"_____ words _____ like a sword, but the tongue

of the _____ brings _____."

If your desire is to tell your offender exactly how you feel with little regard as to how it might be received, review Week 4.

PLACING BLAME

Sometimes we are itching to confront so that the offender will realize just how wrong they are. It may also be a way to vindicate ourselves, to let the world know that it was "their" fault and not our own. Read Matthew 7:1-5.

1. How big is a speck?

2. How does it interfere with your vision?

3. How big is a plank?

4. How does it interfere with your vision?

5. How does a speck and a plank relate to judging others?

6. Have you removed the plank from your eye? If not review Week 7.

GUISE OF CONCERN

Sometimes, as good Christians, we cover up our revenge under the guise of concern. We tell others their faults because we "care about them" and "want them to grow" when we are really just being critical and judgmental. Fill in the blanks for the following verses.

Proverbs 15:18 "A _____ man stirs up _____, but

a _____ man calms a _____."

Jude 16 "These men are _____ and _____; they

follow their own evil desires; they _____ about themselves and

_____ others for their own _____."

We must check our hearts to see if our desire is to stir up or calm down, to find fault and flatter or hold up the mirror so the offender can clearly see the smudge on his face. If the guise of concern is your motive, go back and review Week 8.

PUNISHMENT

Punishment can come in many subtle and not so subtle forms. Confrontation can be a means of exacting punishment while walking away feeling totally justified. Check out these verses and fill in the blank.

Proverbs 10:11 "The _____ of the righteous is a fountain of _____,

but _____ overwhelms the _____ of the wicked."

Proverbs 12:6 "The _____ of the wicked lie in wait for _____,

but the _____ of the upright _____ them."

If you are confronting to bring pain or calamity upon a person, you are in the punishment mode. Review Week 9.

EXPECTATION OF CHANGE/REPENTANCE

The final heart check is the most difficult. When we fantasize about the perfect confrontation, we are eloquent in speech, the offender is moved to tears by our words and falls on his knees in repentance, never to sin again. As I said, this is fantasy, not reality. But it is difficult to let go of this picture. It is good and right to want to see the repentance of our offender. It is also good to want to motivate them towards that repentance. The problem comes when we step over the line of being a tool and take on the role of surgeon. We are the tools that God often uses, but He is the only surgeon capable of doing a spiritual heart transplant. If we go into confrontation expecting that we will bring about change in another's life, we are sure to be disappointed. The change will not be as great, as deep, or as obvious as we think it should be. We must hope for change, but realize that God is capable of using other circumstances in addition to the confrontation to complete the operation.

QUESTIONS TO ASK YOURSELF:

1. Why do I want to confront?

2. What do I want to see happen?

3. How will I feel if my desire is not fulfilled?

DAY 2—CONFRONTATION MEANS LOVE AND SACRIFICE

What is confrontation? Is it a knockdown, drag-out fight? Is it a yelling match? Is it a presentation of a problem and then ducking the bullets that come in defense? Most people do not like confrontation because of the above views, but confrontation does not have to include any of those behaviors.

Confrontation is simply an opportunity for repentance. Opportunity is the operative word. Confrontation does not guarantee repentance, nor does it promise to be painless. Confrontation must be done out of a motive of love for the other person, and a desire to see them set free from the bondage of their sin. It is giving a key to your offender and allowing him to unlock the chains that bind him and keep him from loving others without harm.

Confrontation (the giving of the key) is often risky business. The chains have usually chafed the offender's wrists and made it painful for him to reach out to receive. In the pain of reaching, he may refuse the key and strike out at the giver, believing you to be the source of pain instead of the chains that bind him. Or he may simply turn away, refusing to reach for the gift of freedom because he is too afraid of the agony he may experience in the process of being set free.

In order to confront, we must be willing to sacrifice. It is a sacrifice to confront with pure motives, not expecting any personal gain, but hoping, wishing, desiring for the gain of freedom for our offender. Sometimes it is a sacrifice of pseudo-peace and superficial harmony. We go to family reunions with the offender or even to church and pretend that everything is okay. When we contemplate confrontation, those closest to us counsel against it: "Don't rock the boat." "You don't want to ruin a good time do you?" Or "Wait until Grandma passes on. This would just kill her." The reality is that the boat is already rocking, no one is having a good time and Grandma probably already knows and is stronger than you think. But it is a sacrifice to go to your offender and say, "Excuse me, but I see you have some chains around you. Would you like a key to unlock them?"

Sometimes confrontation is a sacrifice to even be in the presence of the offender. You don't go to the family reunions anymore or to that church or that gathering of friends if the offender is going to be there. Sometimes it truly is dangerous to confront our offender. Confrontation may be dangerous to our reputation, our heart, or even our physical safety. Confrontation does not always have to be face to face or done in private. A letter, a well-used park or restaurant can be a safe setting for a dangerous confrontation. Just because it might be dangerous does not mean that you are exempt from this step. Let's look at a man in the Bible who risked much in order to confront. Read II Samuel 11:27 to 12:14.

1.   What did the Lord think of David's actions with Bathsheba?

2.   Why did Nathan go to David?

3.   What does this tell us about Nathan's motives?

Nathan went to David out of obedience to the Lord. He had no hidden agendas or selfish ambition, his motives were pure. Because he loved the Lord and loved David, he desired to see his relationship restored to God.

4.   What are your motives in confronting your offender?

5.   What was the legal penalty for adultery and murder? (Lev. 20:10, 24:17)

6.   Was Nathan more concerned about the law or David's relationship with God?

Nathan's concern was for David's spiritual well being. Nathan was not as interested in the law, (which required that David and Bathsheba be stoned) as he was in David's relationship with the Lord. His desire was for David's restoration with God, which was in David's best interest.

7.   Who else knew about the affair and murder plot? (II Sam. 11:2-4, 6, 14)

8.   Who else confronted David?

9.   What risks did Nathan take in confronting the king?

10.   Where does your interest lie in confronting your offender?

There were several sacrifices that Nathan made in confronting the king. Many others knew of the king's sin, but chose to keep their mouths shut and lived with the status quo. No one else had opposed or confronted the sin. They ignored it, not wanting to rock the boat. Nathan sacrificed pseudo-peace and superficial harmony in order to bring justice to the land. It was also a sacrifice for Nathan to even be in the presence of the king when he confronted David. Nathan could have been killed by the king for saying things against his character. Other prophets had been killed for such accusations.

11. What would you be sacrificing in confronting your offender?

DAY 3—MEANS OF SOLIDIFYING RELATIONSHIPS

Confrontation has several possible positive outcomes. When there is repentance due to confrontation, confrontation becomes a means of solidifying the relationship. The relationship can deepen as a result of it, developing deeper trust and commitment.

Even when there is no repentance, confrontation is positive in that it is a means of imparting grace to the offender. Author, Dan Allender says, "It is not contradictory to love someone, desire their good, and equally work toward destroying their cancer through bringing them to repentance and faith."[3] Confrontation is the scalpel that exposes the life-threatening cancer of sin that is hidden beneath the healthy skin of our spiritual blindness.

Below is a graph called a Johari Window, named after Joseph Luft and Harry Ingham. It was first used in an information session at the Western Training Laboratory in Group Development in 1955.

The first box is full of information, insights and knowledge that is common to everyone about you. Box number two is information, insights and knowledge known to others, but not to you. Box number three is information, insights and knowledge that is known only to you and no one else. Box number four is the blind box—information, insights and knowledge about you known only by God.

1. Things everyone knows about me.	2. Things others know about me.
3. Things only I know about me.	4. Things only God knows about me.

The goal in confrontation is to increase box 1 and decrease boxes 2, 3 and 4. When we share what we know about others, as God directs, in a loving and compassionate way, it imparts grace to them. It gives them the opportunity to repent and be changed forever by the grace of God.

This is what Jesus did for Peter after the resurrection. The disciples had returned to their former profession of fishing. After fishing all night, catching nothing, they headed for shore, weary and disappointed. Jesus showed up, told them where to cast their nets (deja vu) and then fed them breakfast. This was encounter number three with their risen Lord and Jesus had not yet addressed Peter's sin. Read John 21:15-22.

1.   What did Jesus ask Peter?

2.   How many times did He ask the question?

3.   How many times did Peter deny Jesus? (John 13:38)

4.   What was Jesus' command after each of Peter's replies?

5.   How did this impart grace to Peter?

6.   Compare this encounter with Jesus' initial calling of Peter in Luke 5:1-11.

7.   What information, knowledge or insight do you need to share with your offender in order to impart grace to him or her?

DAY 4—WHEN WE DON'T CONFRONT

Most of the time we are not eager to confront. It is too much of a sacrifice and we are afraid of the repercussions. If we rock the boat too much, the waves may flip the boat and we could drown in the process. However, if we do not confront, we are missing out on a fantastic opportunity. Read Galatians 6:1.

1.   Who is the one being confronted?

2. When you are caught by something, do you want to be there?

3. How easy is it to get away by yourself?

4. What is the goal of the confrontation?

Now read James 5:14-16 and 19-20.

5. The word "sick" in verse 14 literally means "to be weak" and the term "sick person" in verse 15 means "to be weary." Therefore, it does not seem that James is strictly speaking of physical illness, but spiritual and emotional weakness or faintness. In light of this translation, what happens when we restore one who has wandered from the faith (verses 19-20)?

6. In contrast, what can happen if we choose not to confront?

7. How does the view of "caught in sin" and "spiritual weariness" change your perspective of your offender?

Most of the time we do not view our offender as someone in a trap from which they cannot escape. Our culture encourages this view because we value "pulling ourselves up by our own bootstraps." We are an independent society and hate to admit we need others' help. Therefore, we often disdain others who need our help, viewing them as weak, lazy or untouchable. When we refuse to give the help of confrontation, we may be robbing the offender of an opportunity to repent and experience grace, leaving him trapped by the web of sin and weary of the struggle to escape.

Sometimes we don't confront because it does not seem like the loving thing to do. It would rock the boat and make others uncomfortable. Others would even say that it is unchristian because it's just not nice. Read Proverbs 27:5-6.

8. What is better than hidden love?

9.   How have you hidden your love?

10.   What can be trusted?

11.   What does an enemy do?

When a surgeon removes cancer that is killing the patient, he must wound the patient by cutting her open before the cancer can be removed. To kiss away cancer like a child's boo-boo is not only unkind, but fatal.

12.   Who do you need to confront? Make a list and indicate which confrontations should be in person and which should be written in a letter, e-mail or journal.

DAY 5—FOR INSTANCE...

Now that we have discussed the reasons and motivations for confrontation, let's look at a plan for confrontation. Read Matthew 18:15-17.

1.   Who do we confront?

2.   Under what circumstances should you confront?

3.   Should you confront someone who has not sinned against you?

4.   Who should be present at the first confrontation?

5.   When do you bring others into the picture?

6.   When do you make the offense public?

7.   Have you confronted your offender?

8.   If so, was it publicly or privately? If not, what is your plan of confrontation?

9.   Did you bring others into the confrontation? If so, when?

10. If you have not and need to, whom can you ask to be present?

11. Have you brought the matter before a body of believers?

12. If not, what body can you bring it before?

Now it's the time to put feet on the things we have been learning. Pick a believing offender that you feel you are ready to confront. Go back to Day 1 of this chapter and review the heart checks for confrontation. If you can check them all off, then you are ready to write a confrontation. Be prepared to share this letter with your group.

If you have completed all the steps of Matthew 18 and there is still no repentance, the instruction is to treat them as an unbeliever. The next chapter will cover confrontation of the unbeliever.

STEP 6 PART II— CONFRONTING THE UNBELIEVER

DAY 1—WHAT ABOUT JUSTICE?

What does the woman do whose husband has killed her child? What does the husband do whose wife was raped? What about the child who is molested or the college student who was killed by a drunk driver? Where does justice fit in with forgiveness? Are they on opposite sides of the poles, or is there a connection between the two?

On September 11, 2001, our country experienced a horrible violation to our sense of safety, our way of living, and our very lives. In the wake of this massacre, there are many who are confused over the issues of justice versus forgiveness. Our president and even many religious leaders are earnestly seeking justice, yet there are many others who are preaching forgiveness.

Justice and forgiveness are not mutually exclusive. In fact, they are married to each other. Justice without forgiveness twists justice into retaliation, vengeance, or revenge. It distorts the godly characteristic of justice into a satanic means of having your own way. If God did not provide forgiveness for us, His wrath would totally annihilate us and He would be justified in His actions. But for us humans, to have justice without forgiveness would distort our nature into a demonic hunger for revenge. It is demonic in that the desire for revenge consumes us, rather than us being consumed by a passion for truth, righteousness and reconciliation – the passions of God.

On the other hand, forgiveness without justice renders it impotent. The power in forgiveness lies in the knowledge that the offender deserves retribution, yet does not receive the full extent that he deserves. When we as sinners recognize the full extent to which we deserve to be punished, and realize that God's forgiveness has rescued us from that punishment, it transforms our inner being in a way that nothing else can. But when we are unaware of the fullness of His wrath, we discount God's forgiveness as nothing more than a platitude.

Take some time to journal about how you have viewed justice and forgiveness as separate entities and how you now see their relationship. Jot down any questions you may have about their relationship. Now apply this to your offender.

DAY 2—FORGIVENESS, JUSTICE, SALVATION AND VENGEANCE

Yesterday we discussed the marriage of justice and forgiveness. Today we will look at Scriptures that illuminate the interaction between justice and forgiveness.

Read Galatians 3:10-13

1.   Why are we under a curse?

2.   Is there anything we can do to justify ourselves?

3.   How did Christ redeem us?

Read Romans 3:25-26.

4.   Who took the punishment for our sins?

5.   How are we justified?

6.   How do you see forgiveness and justice working together through the blood of Jesus?

Read Isaiah 59:12-20.

7.   Why is no one available to bring justice?

8.   Why was the Lord displeased?

9.   What appalled Him?

10. What did He do?

11. How do salvation, righteousness and vengeance work together?

12. How are salvation, righteousness and vengeance affecting your offender?

We may never see the effects of God's vengeance on our offender on this earth. God's vengeance comes in many different ways. It can be physical, financial, emotional, relational or spiritual. The emotional and spiritual vengeance are the most difficult to identify. But God has promised to exact vengeance because it is part of justice.

What if the offender is repentant? What happens to vengeance? God's wrath is then poured out on His Son who became the curse for our offenders. According to God's laws, the penalty must be paid for sin. Someone always pays the price.

As I was preparing for this section, the realization that someone must pay the price really made me angry. It did not seem fair or just, but that is the nature of forgiveness. We choose to pay a price for our offenders' actions. In reality, we pay a very small price. The ultimate price was and is paid by the innocent Lamb who was slain for our sins and the sins of our offenders. Both our offenders and we have the privilege of choosing to pay our own price or allowing God to pick up the tab.

DAY 3—SAGES AND FOOLS

We treat family members differently than we do non-family members. Family receives a little more grace, endurance and patience simply because we're stuck with them. Non-family members do not receive the same privileges. Scripture tells us to treat believers differently from unbelievers. The previous chapter taught us how to treat believers who have offended us. Today we will look at how to treat unbelievers. This includes "believers" who have been confronted via Matthew 18 and have refused to repent.

Psalms and Proverbs have specific names for believers and unbelievers. Psalm 111:10 says, "The fear of the Lord is the beginning of wisdom." Thus, throughout Psalms and Proverbs, the believer is referred to as "wise" or a "wise man." An unbeliever is one who does not fear God. Psalm 14:1 says, "The fool says in his heart, 'There is no God.'" Therefore, the Bible calls an unbeliever a fool. Today we will see how the Scripture tells us to treat those who are wise and those who are foolish.

Read Proverbs 9:7-9.

1. What happens when you confront a fool?

2. What happens when you confront a wise man?

3. As you have confronted people in the past, who has been foolish and who has been wise?

4. How do you respond when you're confronted?

Read Proverbs 14:9.

5. What do fools think about making amends?

6. What should be your expectations in confronting a fool?

Read Proverbs 19:25 and 29.

7. How do fools learn?

8. How do the wise learn?

Confrontation is necessary to find out if our offender is foolish or wise. Once it has been established that your offender is a fool, lower your expectations. Do not expect amends. Matthew 7:6 tells us not to cast our pearls before swine, for they will trample them and attack us in retaliation. Sometimes the only way that repentance will come is through experiencing physical consequences for the violation. Those consequences come in many different packages. It may include physical, relational and/or emotional boundary setting. It may even include bringing the matter to our justice system. The next day's study will cover when to take a person to court. If the offense is not a legal issue, two books that will help in setting boundaries are <u>Boundaries</u> by Townsend and Cloud and <u>Bold Love</u> by Dan Allender.

DAY 4—TAKING PEOPLE TO COURT

Taking people to court is a sticky issue. First Corinthians 6 tells us not to take a believer to court because we are not to "air our dirty laundry" with those outside the family nor are we to submit ourselves to unbelievers. Instead we are to appoint judges within our church who will decide what is right. However, it does not say we cannot take unbelievers to court, and Jesus even told the story of the woman who pestered the king about her case until he gave her justice. Read Matthew 5:6.

1. What are we to hunger and thirst after?

2. Some translations use the word justice instead of righteousness and the Greek word *dikaiosune* can mean either one.[7] How can you hunger and thirst after justice?

Read Romans 13:1-5.

3. Who placed governing authorities in their positions?

4. What is the authority's purpose as God's servant?

5. What is the difference in taking someone to court and taking revenge?

When we take justice into our own hands it becomes revenge. Allowing and supporting those in authority, whom God has called and commissioned, to carry out justice is righteous. Righteousness is agreeing with God as to what is right and wrong. When we remove justice, we call wrong right and allow evil to flourish.

So whom can we take to court? We can sue unbelievers. We can also use the legal system when we have exhausted all of the steps of Matthew 18 with no repentance since we are then told to treat the person as an unbeliever.

When should we take another to court? This is a more difficult question. When there has been a law broken, (a criminal offense) then it is right to utilize the legal system that God established. Even though you can legally take anyone to court for anything, this may not be wise. There are three probable consequences if you lose: 1) you have to pay your own attorney's fees, 2) you have to pay the defender's attorney's fees, and 3) you lose the case. A civil suit is all about money. If you are not seeking revenge through exacting payment, but instead are looking for payment for damage done, a civil suit may not be an ungodly response. For example, a person who has incurred medical bills that he cannot pay due to a car accident has every right to sue the insurance company for refusing payment. To sue for more than the bills total is revenge. It all boils down to **motive**.

If you are considering taking someone to court, there are three things to be done. First, review the motives for confrontation in Week 11, Day 1. Make sure that your motive is not to have a place to vent your emotions, a stage to place blame, for punishment, or an expectation of change. It is important to be sure that the forgiveness process has been completed before going to court. Many relatives who have lost a loved one to violent murder have been interviewed after witnessing the execution of the murderer. Those who had forgiven the criminal were at peace before and after the execution. Those who had not forgiven were sorely disappointed at the lack of satisfaction found after the execution. **There will never be enough justice on this earth to bring satisfaction without forgiveness.**

Once your motives have been worked through, then take a lot of time to pray and be sure that the Holy Spirit is leading you in this direction. If God is not the one leading you, the path will not bring you peace. There are many people, including believers, who would encourage suing any and everyone, but this path is not for everyone to walk.

Finally, be prepared emotionally should you lose your case. Remember, even though God has appointed our judges, they are human, fallible and sometimes even evil themselves. Total justice is not found in court. I have a friend who is a court reporter and she has seen hundreds of thousands of cases and states that no one is ever completely satisfied with the outcome in a court of law. God is truly the only perfect Vindicator.

DAY 5—TRUST IN THE LORD

Today concludes our study of forgiveness. It has been a long and sometimes painful journey. If there was only one truth about forgiveness you could take with you, I would wish that trust in the Lord would sink deep into your heart. Forgiveness is essentially a trust issue. It is not trusting your offender or trusting the church or the legal system, but trusting in the Lord. Let's study Psalm 37 today to learn more about trusting the Lord.

1.   What do we fret about?

2. What does it lead to? (Verse 8)

3. What are the seven alternatives?

   _____ in the Lord (Verse 3)

   _____ yourself in the Lord (Verse 4)

   _____ your _____ to the Lord (Verse 5)

   Be _____ and wait _____ for God (Verse 7)

   Refrain from _____ (Verse 8)

   Turn from _____ (Verse 27)

   _____ for the Lord and keep _____ way (Verse 34)

4. What will God do?

   _____ you the _____ of your heart (Verse 4)

   Make your _____ shine (Verse 6)

   _____ off evil men (Verse 9)

   Give you an _____ (Verse 11)

   _____ the heart of the _____ (Verse 14-15)

   _____ the righteous (Verse 17)

   Break the _____ of the wicked (Verse 17)

   Provide _____ in times of need (Verse 19)

   Make your enemies _____ (Verse 20)

   Make your steps _____ (Verse 23)

   _____ you with His right _____ (Verse 24)

   Love the _____ (Verse 28)

P_____ (Verse 28 & 33)

_____ the righteous (Verse 39)

Be a _____ in time of trouble (Verse 39)

_____ you (Verse 40)

I have seen Psalm 37 work in my own life. Many years ago I worked in a substance abuse rehabilitation center and was asked to do some things that were illegal and unethical. After trying unsuccessfully to explain to my employer why I did not want to carry out his instructions, I sent a letter to the licensing board and gave a copy to my employer. I was promptly fired, but the center was investigated for other complaints as well as my own. Today the center is no longer in existence and the other counselors and administrators who complied are no longer in the mental health profession in this area. They have "...vanish[ed] like smoke." I have looked for them and they cannot be found. But God has blessed me with a master's degree, a successful career in the mental health field, and the ability to lead seminars and write this book. God really does bless and vindicate the righteous. Our job is to trust Him and look for His hand in every circumstance.

I hope that you have grown as a result of this study and that it will be a resource for you to return to again and again. Most people who have been through the study go back through the course on their own or they return to another group for a refresher. As forgiveness deepens, more of your heart is revealed and healed. Forgiveness is more than a process. It is a lifetime challenge. The more you practice the better you become.

FORGIVE
and
LIVE

Leader's
Guide

INTRODUCTION TO LEADER'S GUIDE

Group dynamics measure a group's success. Creating a dynamic group is just as important or more important than the material used by that group. The following suggestions are to help in creating the best cohesion, openness and depth of sharing.

Group Covenant: This is an agreement between group members for confidentiality and other things like starting and finishing on time, letting others speak, not interrupting, etc. An example is provided in the appendix and may be modified for your particular group. This may be copied or reproduced with variations that apply to your particular group.

A major ingredient in a successful group is confidentiality. It is important that all members understand what confidentiality is and its necessity. Confidentiality is an agreement between members that what is said within the group will stay within the group. This means that group members will not discuss others' issues outside of group, even with another group member. Two exceptions include:

(1) All group leaders reserve the right to discuss matters disclosed by group members for the purpose of receiving supervision and oversight. This oversight will occur in group supervision meetings held by the group coordinator and attended by other group leaders. (This may or may not apply to your particular group situation, but if it does, it needs to be included in your explanation of confidentiality to your group.)

(2) Any group members who disclose intentions to take harmful, dangerous, or criminal action against another human being or against themselves will necessitate warnings to appropriate individuals of such intentions. Suspected acts of child abuse or neglect will be reported. Those warned may include a variety of such persons as:

- The person or family of the person who is likely to suffer the results of harmful behavior.
- The family of the group member who intends to harm him or herself or someone else.
- Associates or friends of those threatened or making threats.
- Law enforcement officials or child protection services.

In my experience of leading groups in forgiveness, I have found that 2 situations greatly help the success of the group. The first is when the group becomes closed 2 weeks after starting. This allows for some late-comers, but in order for the group to achieve trust, openness and vulnerability, it is best that there is a cut off of new members after the second group meeting.

The second situation that will help the success of the group is if group members have like circumstances, such as all members being survivors of divorce, adult children of alcoholics, victims of childhood sexual abuse, abused spouses, recovering addicts, spouses of addicts, or those needing anger management. This eliminates shame, embarrassment and pride, which may prevent group members from being real, genuine and vulnerable. When circumstances are varied, people tend to stay on the surface and not disclose the real issues at hand. Group members will receive more healing and freedom and feel more comfortable disclosing the details of their issues when they realize they are not alone in their situation.

There are situations when closing the group or having a homogenous group is not an option. This is usually in a church cell group setting. If there is already relationship established within the group, leaving it open for newcomers or having diverse issues is not as detrimental to the group's success as if the group was being newly established. Often in well-established groups, they are already sharing their wounds and finding acceptance, regardless of their differences.

Another suggestion is that if your group has more than 10 group members, after the review of each week, break up into smaller groups of 4-6 for discussion. Keeping these groups consistent will develop trust and vulnerability. Make sure that you have a leader for each small group.

Another final factor that will greatly enhance your experience is to make sure that you have several people praying for you as a leader and for your group. Unforgiveness is a major stronghold in many people's lives and the enemy is not willing to easily give up this territory. He will come against the one(s) trying to tear down his fortress, but God is greater and has given us weapons of warfare (Eph. 6). My and others' experience in leading this study is that the group and the leader's personal life is much easier when there is consistent protective prayer.

An evaluation is provided in the appendix to help you find what worked and what didn't in your group. This is useful information if you are planning subsequent groups.

HOW TO USE THIS GUIDE

Each week, except for the Introductory Week, a summary of the previous week's homework will be given. There will also be 10 questions provided for group discussion. Five of these questions will address Scriptural principles included in the homework. The other five will be taken from application questions covered during the week. The number of each question correlates with each day of the homework. Question #1 of both the principle and personal questions correlate with Day 1 of the homework given the previous week, question #2 with Day 2, and so on.

Each group meeting should involve a review of the previous week provided in the summary. Leaders should allow time for questions group members may have about the homework, including clarifications, misunderstandings or disagreements. Included in each week is a group exercise to drive home the main point of each week. These group exercises are optional and their effectiveness may depend on the dynamics of your particular group. If you have a large group of 10 or more, some of these exercises are best done during the small group time. Some exercises involve a time of individual work to later be shared with the group. During the individual work it would be helpful to have some music playing softly.

After the group exercise, the principle and personal questions should be addressed. The leader may choose to alternate between principle and personal questions, or cover all principle questions first and then discuss the personal questions. The leader may choose the order depending on the needs of the group.

Answers to the homework questions are included at the end of each chapter in the Leader's Guide. Those questions that are labeled N/A indict that the question is a personal application with no right answer.

INTRODUCTORY WEEK

In the first meeting, the group covenant and confidentiality should be discussed thoroughly. After the leader is assured that each member understands and agrees with the group covenant and confidentiality, then group members can introduce themselves and answer the question, "What has brought you to a group on forgiveness?"

The rest of the group time should be spent covering the "Foundations of Forgiveness" included in the workbook section. It may be read or put into your own words. If read, you may use my personal examples or share those from your own experience. This is foundational material for the rest of the study, so it is important that each group member thoroughly understands this material. At the end of the meeting assign Week 1 as homework.

GROUP EXERCISE

Have each person list what kind of vehicle they are driving, who is in the vehicle, who is driving, how far they are from home and what the terrain looks like (i.e. a desert, a valley, slippery slopes, etc.) Some of the group members may have abandoned their cars and begun the journey home. Where are they in the journey?

Note: If you have a large group, it would be best to do this exercise during the small group time.

WHAT HAPPENS WHEN WE DON'T FORGIVE?

REVIEW

This week has focused on the biblical reasons that God calls unforgiveness "sin" and the consequences of unforgiveness. Unforgiveness takes us back to original sin in wanting to be our own God. We want to be judge, jury, prosecuting attorney, and executioner, if we can get away with it. When in that place, we condemn ourselves and show contempt for God's kindness and mercy.

The consequences of unforgiveness include:

- God not forgiving you
- open door for Satan
- tied to offender
- separation from God and others you love
- higher risk of cancer, burnout and migraines
- quenching the Spirit
- cycle of anger and guilt

GROUP EXERCISE

Materials needed:

1. A bench or row of chairs
2. Fruit of the Spirit, Fruit of the Flesh and "Self" labels. The Fruit of the Spirit includes love, joy, peace, patience, kindness, goodness, faithfulness, gentleness, and self-control (Gal. 5:22-23). The Fruit of the Flesh includes sexual immorality, impurity, debauchery, idolatry, witchcraft, hatred, discord, jealousy, fits of rage, selfish ambition, dissension factions, envy, drunkenness, and orgies (Gal. 5:19-21).
3. Narrator

Depending on the size of the group and the length of the bench, place a label or labels on volunteers. If you have a small group, put three fruits on each person, except the person wearing the "self" label. The narrator should use the following script or an adaptation thereof. The volunteers should act according to the script of the narrator.

Narrator: "When we give our lives to Christ, we have the potential to be full of the Spirit, and that is seen through the Fruit of the Spirit reigning in our hearts. (The Fruit of the Spirit should then sit on the bench.) However, as we allow unforgiveness to build in our hearts, self takes over and begins pushing the Fruit out. (Self should take the place at the end of the bench and begin sliding across the bench until all Fruit has been knocked off.) For a short time we enjoy the throne in our heart, but we are seldom alone for long. Soon the Fruit of the Flesh begins to crowd its way into our heart until we are squeezed out. (The Fruit of the Flesh should take their place on the bench until Self has been pushed off the bench.) We are then left on the floor with the Fruit of the Flesh in control and we are under their feet." (Self should be lying on the floor under the feet of the Fruit of the Flesh.)

As a group, discuss this visual image and how it has played out in their lives.

PRINCIPLE QUESTIONS:

1. Why is God the only one allowed to judge?
2. Why does God's forgiveness of us hinge on our forgiveness of others?
3. How does unforgiveness affect our intimacy with God?
4. How does God treat unforgiving people?
5. How does the armor of God aid us in forgiving others?

PERSONAL QUESTIONS:

1. How has judging others affected your compassion?
2. What does Satan tell you to keep you from forgiving?
3. How has fear affected your relationship with your offender? How has it affected your relationship with those you love?
4. How are you being tortured by unforgiveness?
5. What can you do to let God fight your battle?

ANSWERS TO HOMEWORK

DAY 1

1. A judge determines who is right or wrong and the penalty due.
2. A judge must know the law, be just and fair, impartial, and not biased.
3. A judge can be disqualified from a case if he has relationship with either party in the case.
4. God's job

5. You sit in judgment of the law, and you get judged with the same measurement.
6. It's not our job.
7. It's God's job to judge, He is the lawgiver, and He is the only One justified.
8. Consequences of judging others include condemning self, despising God's kindness, and reaping God's judgment.
9. Judging others puts a wall between God and us and puts us in the defendant's seat.
10. When we show contempt for God's kindness, we become goats.

DAY 2

1. To be God
2. We want to be God.
3. Satan questioned God's goodness and made it seem God was withholding something good.
4. N/A
5. N/A
6. It blocks God's forgiveness for our sins and blocks our relationship with Him.
7. It takes us away from Him.
8. Because we are trying to take God's place.

DAY 3

1. By the words of their mouths.
2. No
3. N/A
4. That God loved us and sacrificed His Son for us.
5. Because God loved us first, He lives in us, and His love is made complete in us.
6. Living in God, His Spirit and reliance on God's love.
7. No
8. No
9. N/A
10. N/A

DAY 4

1. Millions of dollars to a few dollars.
2. It distresses them.
3. Wicked, he did not give as had been given to him, he was ungrateful.
4. Bondage and torture.
5. N/A
6. Satan
7. N/A
8. We walk into his prison when we don't forgive.

DAY 5

1. No, it's a fact of life. The sin comes with what we do with our anger or how long we allow it to continue, letting it grow into resentment and bitterness.
2. Unwholesome talk, grieving the Holy Spirit, bitterness, rage, brawling, slander, malice, etc.
3. Bitterness, rage, brawling, slander, malice, etc.
4. Reputation, joy, life, love, freedom—not just from the one we're angry with, but with innocent bystanders close to us.
5. Prayer, armor of God, His mighty power, perspective—not at war with flesh but a spiritual battle.
6. Stand firm and pray.
7. N/A
8. God
9. N/A

RESTORATION

Many of the group members are not at a place of restoration yet. Please assure them that as long as they are in the process of forgiveness, if they have stepped out of the car, they are on the right road. Desiring restoration is the fifth step in a six-step process. They may still be on step one. The purpose of this week's study is not to condemn or set an unrealistic expectation but to show the difference between forgiveness and restoration.

REVIEW

This week the study covered the difference between forgiveness and restoration. Forgiveness is solely dependent on the victim. Restoration is dependent on the **victim's forgiveness and the offender's repentance**. Restoration means to return to a changing/repentant relationship in order that it may become deeper and healthier than before the hurt.

Repentance is not regret. Regret is sorrow for getting caught, sorrow that the victim was hurt, but no responsibility is taken for the hurtful event. Repentance is characterized by these 7 traits:

1. A broken and contrite heart
2. A willingness to take responsibility for their own behavior
3. A willingness not to offend again
4. Not out of self-pity nor a martyr syndrome
5. Does not throw guilt or blame onto the one offended
6. Not out of anger but out of humility
7. Claims no rights while asking mercy for a wrong done

(A comparison of a broken person and a proud person is in your appendix. This may be copied and used in your group session. It would be most beneficial to use the list to assess not only the offender, but also the victim, in order to give perspective.)

The second characteristic, a willingness to take responsibility for their own behavior, means that they own the sin and expect consequences. They do not expect to be bailed out or let off the hook.

In being willing not to offend again, the person is willing to do whatever it takes not to offend again. The offender is willing to submit to another for help to change whether this means going to counseling, finding an accountability partner and/or someone to disciple them.

Repentance is not motivated out of self-pity or a martyr syndrome. Statements like, "It's always my fault;" "I'm such a failure;" "I can't ever do anything right;" are really excuses not to change or to take responsibility.

Repentance does not blame-shift or throw guilt back on the one offended. "If you hadn't done..." or "If only you had..." does not constitute a repentant heart. No one can make us do anything or respond in any way without our permission. In other words, no matter the actions or inactions of others, each person is responsible for their own behavior.

The sixth characteristic of repentance is that it is not done out of anger but out of humility. This compliments the first characteristic. Sometimes a person can say all the right things, but the attitude of anger is very prevalent. It is almost as if they feel that they are forced into repentance and resent the whole ordeal, but have no other choice. My oldest child often falls into this category. After discipline, we pray with our children so that they can ask for forgiveness from God for their wrong. Frequently my oldest will say the right words, but with an attitude of anger and resentment. It is then that we tell her, "You are not ready to pray. Stay where you are until you are ready." Sometimes she is there for a little while, usually she is there for a long while, and sometimes it takes giving her scripture to read until God breaks through to her and her heart is truly repentant.

The last characteristic is claiming no rights while asking mercy for a wrong done. When David repented of adultery and murder, he did not claim any rights of his kingship. In other countries and cultures, a king could have any woman he wanted. He was simply grateful that God let him live.

When forgiveness has been granted and repentance has occurred, then restoration is possible. The steps of restoration are as follows:

1. Testing repentance
2. Building trust
3. Reaffirmation of love
4. Stop sandbagging
5. Resuming the relationship

These steps have been thoroughly discussed in the homework.

GROUP EXERCISE

Materials needed:

1. Cardboard boxes of various sizes
2. Markers

Using cardboard boxes as bricks, label each brick with an attitude, feeling or characteristic from the Broken People vs. Proud People chart in the appendix and Seven Characteristics of Repentance. For example, you may have bricks that say, "Blaming," "Focus on failure," or "Comparing self with others." Instruct group members to use these bricks to build bridges or walls to demonstrate their defensiveness or receptiveness towards their offender. Ask those who are willing to share their bridge or wall with the group.

PRINCIPLE QUESTIONS:

1. What struck you as unique about David's confession?
2. How did Joseph test his brothers' repentance?
3. How did God build trust with Gideon?
4. How did Gideon prove his trustworthiness with God?
5. Why is it important to reaffirm our love to our offender?

PERSONAL QUESTIONS:

1. How do your confessions compare with David's?
2. How have you tested your offender's repentance?
3. Why would your offender not trust you? What have you done to build trust?
4. What has your offender done to prove his trustworthiness to you?
5. Some of you have not done any of the above steps because you have not resumed the relationship. Why are you afraid to resume the relationship?

Some group members have not resumed the relationship because it is dangerous to do so. Others have not because there was really no relationship before the offense. Both are legitimate reasons. If there have been no signs of repentance and the offender is danger-ous physically, then it is best to look for signs of repentance from a distance, like Joseph did. If there was no relationship prior to the offense, then there is nothing to restore.

ANSWERS TO HOMEWORK

DAY 1

1. David showed a broken and contrite heart by asking for mercy and acknowl-edging his sin and his desperate need for God's cleansing power. (Ps. 51:1-3, 7, 10, 16-17)
2. David showed he was willing to take responsibility for his behavior by not placing blame on another and by saying he was constantly aware of his sin. (Ps. 51:4)

3. David showed he didn't want to offend again by asking God to create a new heart in him and wanting to show others who have gone astray the way back to God. (Ps. 51:10,13)

4. David showed his repentance was not out of self-pity nor a martyr syndrome by saying God was justified in His judgment. (Ps. 51:4)

5. David showed he would not shift the blame by not making excuses for his behavior when confronted with his sin. (II Sam. 12:13)

6. David showed his repentance was not out of anger, but humility by acknowledging his need for God, agreement with God that it was sin, not shifting blame, and accepting consequences. (II Sam. 12, Ps. 51)

7. David showed he would not claim any rights while asking mercy for a wrong done by accepting the consequences of his sin. (II Sam. 12:22-23)

DAY 2

1. Joseph was 17 when his brothers sold him into slavery and did not see him again until he was about 30. He was also dressed as an Egyptian and spoke through an interpreter.

2. Benjamin was Joseph's only full brother and Joseph wanted to see how his brother would treat the next favored son.

3. He continued to favor Benjamin, testing the brothers' jealousy. He saw who would sacrifice themselves for Benjamin.

4. Joseph assured his brothers of safety when they were afraid. He saw God's perspective concerning what his brothers did to him. He wept when his brothers asked for forgiveness.

5. No. He cried for them a lot.

6. N/A

7. N/A

DAY 3

1. Hiding in a hole in the ground.

2. Mighty warrior.

3. To save Israel.

4. I am incapable. I don't have what it takes.

5. I will be with you and will fight the battle for you.

6. He had seen the ravaging of his enemies and the suffering of his people. He himself was afraid of his enemy. He had not seen God's hand working for him before.

7. Failing, getting killed.

8. He was faithful to His word and followed through on the signs Gideon asked for.

9. Asked the "angel" to stay until he had returned with an offering. 2. Asked for the fleece to be wet and the ground dry. 3. Asked for the fleece to be dry and the ground wet.

10. N/A

11. N/A
12. N/A

DAY 4

1. Tear down the altars of Baal and Asherah and build a proper altar to the Lord. Go into battle and get rid of 99% of your men.
2. God was testing Gideon's obedience.
3. N/A
4. N/A
5. N/A
6. N/A
7. N/A
8. N/A

DAY 5

1. No.
2. The Lord.
3. Go to Saul and restore his sight.
4. Saul had been killing Christians.
5. N/A
6. The Lord.
7. Ananias called him, "Brother."
8. N/A
9. Dealt with.
10. Yes
11. So he will not be overwhelmed by excessive sorrow.
12. Reaffirm their love for him.
13. So that Satan would not outwit them.
14. N/A

BOUNDARIES

In your group there will be those who really enjoyed this chapter because they will take it as license to divorce, avoid, or cut off relationships. This is not God's heart and they need to be challenged to examine their motives and the softness of their heart. Hardening one's heart toward another human will result in a hardening towards God. How willing are they to obey?

Another segment of the group will have a difficult time with this chapter because they have been taught that love and consequences are diametrically opposed. "This form of excommunication is actually a gift, a respectful choice to honor the abuser with the consequences of his/her own destructive choice, in hope that the loneliness and shame will draw his [or her] cold heart back to the fire of relationship."[9]

REVIEW

In ancient times property lines were marked with stones painted white. These boundary stones were like the pegs put in the ground today by surveyors. If a neighbor came in the night and moved a boundary stone 1 inch one day each week, it would hardly be noticed, but in one month he would have stolen 4 inches of property. Over the course of one year, he would have stolen 4 feet! That's a lot of land!

We also have boundaries around our hearts. When people move those boundary stones, they are actually stealing parts of our hearts! When we push the boundary stones of others, we are taking over parts of their hearts.

David gives us a very good example of boundaries. With the first spear, David eludes Saul twice and later Saul promises not to kill David. With the second spear, David escapes and leaves town. Saul has a spiritual experience and David goes to Jonathan for help to test Saul's repentance. Saul fails the test and David flees.

David later has the chance to kill Saul in a cave, but he leaves it to God. He does, however, confront Saul. Saul has remorse (24:16) but David stays in the desert. David again has a chance to kill Saul in his own camp, confronts Saul, and Saul "repents," but David stays in the desert. This is the last time David sees Saul because Saul dies in battle.

When Saul encroaches on David's boundaries, David confronts him with love, honor and loyalty and it brings shame on Saul. When David hears of Saul's, death he is grieved.

GROUP EXERCISE

Materials needed:

Approximately five white stones and five red stones for each participant.

Give each participant five white stones to represent their boundary markers. Set a pile of red stones in the middle of the group. The color red will represent crossing a boundary. During group discussion, as group members relate incidents of crossing other's boundaries, have group members give each other red stones. For example, Sue talks about her lack of trust in her teenage daughter and looks through her drawers, bookbag and purse to see if she can find evidence of drug use. Those group members that consider that to be crossing boundaries would give Sue a red stone to represent what she has stolen from her daughter. When a participant shares about others crossing his/her own boundary, group members will take that participant's white stones. For example, for a husband whose wife rages while he sits back and takes it, group members would take his white stones. The objective of this exercise is to visually show each participant's boundary difficulty.

Note: If you have a large group, it would be best to do this exercise during the small group time.

PRINCIPLE QUESTIONS

1. Why did Saul lose his kingdom?
2. How did David's focus help him in life?
3. How did David test Saul's intentions?
4. How did David keep his heart soft?
5. What are some guidelines for boundary setting?

PERSONAL QUESTIONS

1. What is your level of obedience?
2. What is your focus?
3. How are you testing your offender?
4. On whom are you relying for vengeance and protection?
5. How are you setting up boundaries for you offender? Do they show love, honor and loyalty?

ANSWERS TO HOMEWORK

DAY 1

1. Saul was chosen by God and anointed by Samuel.
2. Saul became king when Samuel anointed him alone.
3. Humble.
4. God was their King and they dethroned Him.
5. To follow the Lord with all their heart.
6. Fear
7. Fear
8. He was not appointed and did not wait for Samuel as instructed.
9. The kingdom was taken from Saul. His descendants would not rule the kingdom.
10. Saul did not obey His instructions.
11. Obedience is better than sacrifice.
12. N/A
13. N/A

DAY 2

1. Private and unexpected.
2. Short, brave.
3. Great looks
4. Great heart.
5. N/A
6. One on one battle for the kingdom.
7. Fear
8. Righteous anger, defiance.
9. David focused on what God could do, Saul focused on what men could do.
10. Military security.
11. So people would think it was Saul. He was concerned for his reputation.
12. David made Saul look good. He was successful at all he did. He wanted to keep him as an ally.
13. David got more credit.
14. N/A

DAY 3

1. Nothing
2. Let the Philistines kill him in battle.
3. It only made David more popular and Saul more fearful.
4. So David would die trying to obtain the bride price.
5. David was very willing to accept Saul at his word. He thought Saul would honor his oath to God as David would.
6. N/A

7. David tested from a distance.
8. N/A

DAY 4

1. In the Lord.
2. The Lord.
3. He had touched the Lord's anointed.
4. Addressed him with respect, bowed / prostrated self, confronted with integrity, honor, and love.
5. N/A
6. The Lord.
7. No
8. Self, reputation, lineage
9. To prove his innocence
10. He thought Saul would die in battle or of natural causes, but regardless David would be delivered
11. 11.No
12. The Lord.
13. He grieved his death.
14. The Lord
15. It grieved him.

DAY 5

1. Be cursed.
2. N/A
3. N/A
4. A fellow believer
5. Better if we can settle the matter privately first.
6. No
7. As an unbeliever
8. Love them, but not have intimacy with them.
9. So sinful nature would be destroyed, but his spirit saved.
10. N/A
11. When we see they are not regarding biblical teaching, blatant disobedience.
12. So they will feel ashamed.
13. N/A
14. N/A

STEP 1—EXAMINING THE HURT

The first step in the forgiveness process was covered this week of **examining the hurt**. This entailed identifying the type of hurt and resolving anger. The types of hurt are:

1. Universal Hurt,
2. Perceived Hurt,
3. Unrealistic expectations and
4. Self-centeredness.

Anger is a by-product of hurt and/or fear and also acts as a barometer to reveal the demands we place on God. The 5 Step process of resolving anger is:

1. Get rid of the energy produced by anger.
2. Identify the event/person that caused the anger.
3. Find the primary emotion that the anger is covering.
4. Find out how the emotion relates to God.
5. Stop nursing it!

The fourth step of finding how the emotion relates to God is a difficult one. There are times in which the anger is a righteous anger—agreement with God—but those times are few and far between. Week 9 will address the difference between righteous anger and man's anger. Most of our anger (99%) falls into the category of man's anger. This anger is a symptom of the demands we put on God. However, this concept is so foreign to most of us that it takes a lot of soul searching to accomplish this step.

One of the frequent questions asked concerning this is about anger when disciplining children. Discipline does not have to involve anger. When my children's disobedience causes me to get angry, it is usually for one of two reasons. The first is that I have waited to discipline until I am angry. The problem lies not so much in their disobedience as in my laziness to discipline at the first sign of disobedience.

The second cause of my anger is the belief that my children's behavior is a reflection of me. If my children obey, then it validates my ability to be a good parent, will cause others to respect me and I'll get some brownie points in heaven. All of these thoughts are based on lies. God, the perfect parent, did everything right in the Garden of Eden, yet His children still disobeyed. Children have their own free will and though this does not give me the freedom to not discipline, it does mean that God holds them accountable for what they know to be wrong.

If people are having trouble with this concept, please encourage them to dig a little deeper. They may need some one-on-one time to fully embrace this idea.

GROUP EXERCISE

Materials need:

1.   Construction paper cut into the shape of food items
2.   Liquid paper correction pens
3.   Clear bowl full of water

Group members will choose several "food" items. Using the Liquid Paper pens, have group members label the "food" with things they tell themselves to feed their anger. These labels may include "He's such a jerk," or "Anger will protect me," or "Last Christmas she…" Have group members place their "food" in the bowl to make "Anger Soup." As the colors bleed into the water, talk about the way the soup looks, how appetizing it is, what it would do to your body if you ate it, how toxic it would be, etc.

Note: If you have a large group, it would be best to do this exercise during the small group time.

PRINCIPLE QUESTIONS

1.   What is the only type of hurt that we forgive?
2.   What are we supposed to do with our anger?
3.   How do we sin in our anger?
4.   What does anger reveal about our relationship with God?
5.   How do your emotions relate to your relationship with God?

PERSONAL QUESTIONS

1.   How many offenses did you discover were really unrealistic expectations or self-centeredness?
2.   Where are you going for comfort and relief from your distress?
3.   How are you nursing your anger?
4.   What demands have you placed on God?
5.   How did this 5 Step process work for your anger?

ANSWERS TO HOMEWORK

DAY 1

Practical application

DAY 2

1. N/A
2. N/A
3. N/A
4. Go to a quiet place and pray.
5. Obedience-broken and contrite heart.
6. It takes trust to obey.
7. N/A
8. N/A
9. N/A

DAY 3

1. N/A
2. Gives the devil a foothold.
3. You play with it, sing to it, cuddle it, don't leave it for very long and it grows.
4. N/A
5. N/A
6. N/A
7. N/A
8. We lie to ourselves.
9. No. We can't slander.
10. A tree with roots.
11. Many people, not just ourselves.
12. N/A

DAY 4

1. Cain brought "some" fruit-average. Abel brought "some from the firstborn"-the best.
2. He was not accepted and became jealous of his brother's acceptance.
3. God
4. Losing God's love, favor, acceptance
5. Took out the competition.
6. By the sea.
7. To pursue them.
8. So that He would be glorified through another defeat.
9. To the Lord.
10. Moses

11. That God would not protect them—that they would die.
12. Aaron and Moses
13. Lack of provision.
14. The Lord
15. No
16. So He could reveal His glory.
17. Not much trust.
18. N/A

DAY 5

Practical Application

ANGER WITH GOD

REVIEW

Last week we did an in-depth study on anger. This week we have looked at our anger at God and the things we blame Him for. There will be some in your group who can freely acknowledge their anger towards God. Others will have difficulty recognizing that there is anger because as children they were not allowed to be angry with God or other authority figures. Those who fall into this category need to be challenged to use the steps in Week 4, specifically identifying the event/person causing the anger. Most likely their anger at God is being taken out on those around them.

There may also be a few individuals in the group who really do not blame God for anything because they have learned a deep trust in the Lord, His sovereignty, and His goodness. For the rest of the group, there are 3 things that tend to incite our anger towards God. They are:

1. Discipline for our wrongdoing.
2. The actions of other people.
3. Unrealistic expectations, which include:
    *   If I am good, nothing bad will happen.
    *   If something bad happens, I must have done something wrong.
    *   If I haven't done anything wrong, then God must be wrong for sending something bad.
    *   Nothing bad will ever happen to those I love. If it does, then God is wrong.

The solutions to the problem of anger at God are:

1. Repentance
2. Perspective
3. Trust/Acceptance
4. Allowing for grief

GROUP EXERCISE

Materials needed:

1. Poster board cut into the shape of a head (2-3 per poster board)
2. Magazines

3. Scissors
4. Glue
5. Colored markers

Give each group member 2 heads. One head will represent the perception of God that they have held throughout their lives. The other head represents what scripture tells us about God. Have group members cut out pictures or words that describe their perception of God and the scriptural view of God and glue them to the appropriate heads. Then group member will discuss their previous view, how it is different from scripture and what they might be able to do to make their perception more in line with scripture.

Note: This exercise is done in the small group setting.

PRINCIPLE QUESTIONS

1. Why does God discipline us?
2. When we blame God for other's choices, what do we accuse God of doing?
3. How can we have both peace and trouble at the same time?
4. How did Job sin in the midst of his suffering?
5. How do repentance, perspective, trust/acceptance, and allowing for grief dissipate our anger at God?

PERSONAL QUESTIONS
1. What is your attitude towards God's discipline?
2. How does your portrait of God compare to the one Scripture paints?
3. What work has God displayed in your life through hardship?
4. How have you condemned God in order to justify yourself?
5. Which of the solutions (repentance, perspective, trust/acceptance, and allowing for grief) do you need to apply to resolve your anger?

ANSWERS TO HOMEWORK

DAY 1

1. God is treating us as His children.
2. For our good.
3. A harvest of righteousness and peace.
4. N/A
5. N/A

DAY 2

1. They could eat from any tree but one.
2. Eve
3. With her.
4. Both ate.
5. Eyes were opened to know good and evil.
6. God and Eve.
7. Giving him defective wife
8. God was withholding from them, seemed to give good things but withheld the best.
9. Adam believed the image that God seemed to give good things but they are really defective. That image caused him to believe that God was at fault.
10. N/A
11. N/A
12. N/A

DAY 3

1. Yes
2. Yes.
3. By remembering that Jesus has overcome the world and that the Father is with us.
4. No one.
5. Either because of his sin or his parents' sin.
6. So that God could be glorified.
7. N/A
8. N/A

DAY 4

1. Self-righteous
2. Charged God with wrongdoing.
3. Confronts Job for accusing Him and condemning God to justify Himself.
4. N/A
5. Repentance
6. N/A
7. Best of friends—loved them deeply.
8. Two more days.
9. Yes
10. Yes
11. Yes
12. He grieved with them.
13. Yes
14. Raising him from the dead.
15. Roll the stone.
16. N/A

DAY 5

1. N/A
2. Being hard pressed, perplexed, persecuted, struck down.
3. By fixing eyes on eternal glory.
4. What is unseen and eternal, not seen and temporary.
5. N/A
6. Suffering leads to perseverance, which leads to character which, leads to hope.
7. Because the end result is hope.
8. Because God has poured out His love into our hearts.
9. He tells us.
10. N/A
11. Safety, desires of our hearts, make righteousness shine, and show the justice of your cause.
12. God. Me.
13. N/A
14. N/A
15. All things.
16. Those He loves and has called.
17. N/A
18. N/A
19. N/A
20. N/A
21. N/A

GUILT, SHAME AND SELF-CONDEMNATION

Beware! The study this week can be even more controversial than last week. This concept of forgiving ourselves has really infiltrated the church, but it feeds a self-sufficiency that is contrary to the gospel.

REVIEW

As mentioned in the Foundations of Forgiveness, we only forgive sin. The question in forgiving ourselves comes down to whether or not we can sin against ourselves. Only one scripture even alludes to sinning against ourselves (I Cor. 6:18-20). If examined carefully, if one is a believer, sexual sin is really a sin against the Lord who resides in us because it defiles His temple. The reality is that when we sin, it is because we believe we will gain something from it. When we don't receive the promised pay-off and realize the devastating effects of our selfish behavior, we dive into guilt. The guilt sometimes becomes so overwhelming that even when we have asked God to forgive us, we don't feel released. Somehow we come to believe that the problem is that we need to forgive ourselves.

The problem with guilt is not solved through forgiving ourselves. In fact, it will only lead to more bondage. Forgiving ourselves drags us deeper into a works mentality, false pride, and fallacious thinking. A works mentality involves using good deeds to make up for the bad ones, hoping that the scale will rest in our favor. False pride is the belief that our sins are more powerful than God's love or grace. It can lead to a practice of penance because of thinking that God's forgiveness is simply not enough to eradicate the sin.

The fallacious thinking that evolves from forgiving ourselves is two-part. One is that "If I was really forgiven, I wouldn't sin anymore," and the other is "If I was really forgiven, there wouldn't be any consequences." The first fallacy is usually found in those with habitual sins or addictions. When they find themselves doing that same old sin again, they berate themselves, giving themselves a mental lashing, and, out of guilt, wind up deeper into the addiction to alleviate the guilty feelings.

The second fallacy involves the mentality that forgiveness and consequences are mutually exclusive. God forgives us, but also disciplines us so that we will learn to follow His ways and not our own. A variation of this fallacy is the confusion between guilt and grief. We may think we are feeling guilty when really we are grieving over the consequences of our sin, the loss of a promised pay-off for sin, the effects of our sin on those around us, or the effects of another's sin on us.

This last point often applies to survivors of sexual abuse. They feel guilty for not telling anyone, for not fighting harder or not fighting at all. They even feel guilty because they believe they must have done something to seduce the perpetrator. These precious people need to be reassured that they are feeling guilty over another's sin, not their own. Much of their "guilty" feeling is really grief over losing their innocence, sense of trust, feelings of safety and numerous other losses. There is a time to grieve and mourn those losses, and then there is a time to move on and allow God to change the grieving into joy. They may need to be referred to professional counseling to discover how God can change their ashes of grief into the beauty of joy.

The problem of guilt is resolved in a 3-step process:

1. Identify the sin, making sure the sin is ours, not someone else's and that it is really is a sin, not a mistake or accident.
2. Confess the sin to God and another person who can proclaim God's forgiveness to us.
3. Remember God's promises to combat the accusation of Satan who loves to trap us in cages of guilt.

GROUP EXERCISE

Materials needed:

1. Potato wafer paper or edible paper. You can write on this paper but it dissolves in water and can be found at a local cake-decorating store.
2. A wooden cross large enough for each member to nail his or her piece of paper to it.
3. A glass bowl full of water dyed red
4. A glass of clear water
5. A towel for drying hands
6. Communion elements

Have group members write on the dissolving paper sins that they struggle believing God has forgiven. Then ask group members to nail their papers to the cross. When every group member is done, have each take a piece of paper from the cross and put it in the bowl of red water representing the blood of Jesus. The paper will dissolve, representing that the sin is no more. Then group members wash their hands in a clear bowl of water to symbolize that they are free from sin. After this process, serve communion.

PRINCIPLE QUESTIONS

1. Why do we sin?
2. How do works and false pride deceive us into believing we can forgive ourselves?
3. What's the difference between false guilt and conviction?
4. What are the steps in receiving God's forgiveness?
5. Why does God give us consequences even though we've been forgiven?

PERSONAL QUESTIONS

1. Can we sin against ourselves?
2. In what ways does a works mentality and false pride keep you from receiving God's forgiveness?
3. How have you experienced the difference between false guilt and conviction?
4. Name some promises you have claimed to fight the accusations of the enemy?
5. How have you confused guilt with grief?

ANSWERS TO HOMEWORK

DAY 1

1. Sin
2. Unrealistic expectations, mistakes, accidents.
3. N/A
4. Sexual immorality.
5. God
6. The Holy Spirit dwells there.
7. Holy Spirit/God, by defiling His temple.
8. Believe we will gain from the sin.
9. Evil desire.

DAY 2

1. Filthy rags.
2. Circumcised on the eighth day, Israelite, Hebrew of Hebrews, able to trace his lineage, Pharisee, persecuted the church, faultless.
3. He compared it to surpassing greatness of knowing Christ.
4. N/A
5. N/A
6. Christ's. He trusts in a righteousness that comes from faith.
7. N/A
8. God

9. No one.
10. Nothing
11. N/A
12. N/A
13. N/A

DAY 3

1. What he does not want to do.
2. What he wants to do.
3. His sinful nature.
4. Godly sorrow.
5. Worldly sorrow.
6. Repentance that leads to salvation.
7. Death
8. Brings an awareness and distaste for the sin thus motivation to change.
9. N/A
10. N/A
11. Search me, know my heart, test me, and know my thoughts.
12. Any offensive way in me.
13. Lead me out of it into His way.

DAY 4

Personal Application

DAY 5

1. Taking a census.
2. Choice of three consequences.
3. Seven years famine, three months of fleeing from your enemies or three days of plague.
4. To fall into the hands of the Lord—he trusted God's mercy, not men's.
5. 70,000 people died.
6. That it affected other people, no victimless sins.
7. Painful
8. A harvest of righteousness.
9. Sign of grief.
10. Sign of grief.
11. In her brother's house, a desolate woman.
12. Bind the brokenhearted, proclaim freedom for the captives, release for prisoners, proclaim year of the Lord's favor, comfort those who mourn, and provide for those who grieve.
13. Crown of beauty.
14. Garment of praise.
15. N/A

STEP 2—SEEKING GOD'S FORGIVENESS

REVIEW

This step is the most important step in the whole forgiveness process. It brings humility, reality, and appreciation for grace into each member's life. Without these qualities it is difficult to forgive.

The first situation we examined was when we were part of the dance. In 90% of the offenses, both parties have some confessing to do. If each would look for their own fault and take responsibility for it, more divorces and civil suits would be resolved outside of the courtroom. However, this action is the hardest on our pride and, thus, the way least traveled. This way is the only way of the cross. God will not allow us to point the finger without eventually dealing with the three fingers pointing back at ourselves.

The second situation is one where there was not a dance, but a wall of protection was built as a result of the offense. Instead of relying on the Lord's protection, we believe the lie that was planted during the offending event; the lie that God is not powerful enough, does not care enough or is too busy with more important things/people to protect us. There are many variations on the lie, but it all boils down to the belief that we must protect and control our world at all costs.

It is a difficult and painful process to tear down the walls of self-protection. They are semi-effective. They do keep people away. The downside is that some of those people are those we want to be close to, including God. As we become proficient in trusting our own protective devices, they become the steps in a dance with others. Repentance and trust are the basics in self-protection demolition. Repentance involves confessing the sin to God, confessing to those we have offended, asking for forgiveness, and praising God for His forgiveness.

GROUP EXERCISE

Materials needed:

1. A red ribbon for each group member
2. A white ribbon for each group member

Place a red ribbon in each chair before the group members arrive. Explain at the end of the session that the red ribbon symbolizes our sin. Ask them to take some time and confess their sin to the Lord. When they are ready, they can individually pray with the leader, confessing their sin. The leader will then pray over the participant, proclaiming God's forgiveness and asking God to help them receive His forgiveness. Take the red ribbon from them and then give them a white ribbon, representing God cleansing us from sin. Make sure that there are enough leaders to pray with each participant and that there is adequate time for this exercise.

Note: If you have a large group, it would be best to do this exercise during the small group time.

PRINCIPLE QUESTIONS

1. Who is responsible for your sin?
2. How was Jesus' teaching different from "an eye for an eye"?
3. What happens when we put our trust in something other than God?
4. How do we obtain righteousness?
5. Why is it important to confess your sins to another human you have offended?

PERSONAL QUESTIONS

1. How well do you play the blame game?
2. How involved in the dance were you with your offender?
3. What has been your favorite mode of self-protection?
4. When you think of your offender being made righteous, how do you feel?
5. Were you able to confess to someone this week? How did it go?

ANSWERS TO HOMEWORK

DAY 1

1. She picked it from the tree.
2. No
3. No
4. From Eve.
5. No
6. No
7. God and Eve
8. The serpent.

DAY 2

1. Whatever he has done must be done to him.
2. Equal retaliation.
3. He taught against retaliation, instead he taught to love and give to your offender.

DAY 3

1. Fierce, foreign, coming unexpectedly, devouring everything.
2. Nothing
3. High fortified walls.
4. The walls will fall down and fail you.
5. So they would learn that their "protection" would fail, only God is the faithful protector.
6. Horses, chariots, bow, sword, wealth, wisdom, prestige/reputation, self, God.
7. Wealth, prestige, wisdom, reputation, self, one's own leadership.
8. Death
9. God

DAY 4

1. Deceitful and beyond cure.
2. No one
3. No one
4. To make us conscious of our sins.
5. Through faith in Christ
6. Yes, through faith in Christ.
7. N/A

DAY 5

Practical Application

STEP 3—BECOMING OTHER-CENTERED

REVIEW

The first half of this Bible study was designed to draw people to look at the condition of their own hearts. We have been motivated to let go of unforgiveness, found the difference between forgiveness and restoration, and examined our anger at our offenders, God and ourselves. This chapter is the beginning of a change from being self-absorbed to becoming other-centered, looking beyond our hurt and into the hurts of others. We become other-centered through two means, humility and compassion

Humility is different from co-dependency. Co-dependency is when I give up my rights in order to gain approval, affection or acceptance from another. Humility, as described in Philippians 2, is giving up my rights for a higher cause, the cause of Christ, and in deference to His Lordship. Co-dependency is very self-centered. Humility is emptying the self and receiving approval, affection, and acceptance from Christ. This allows me to freely give because I am full of Christ instead of being a selfish vacuum. I can be like-minded, put away selfish ambition and vain conceit, consider others better than myself, and look to the interests of others because all I need has been provided through Christ.

Compassion and humility go hand in hand. When we realize that there is nothing we are looking for that we don't already have, we become an extension of Christ in the lives of others. Jonah forgot about humility and therefore lost his compassion. He cared more for the bush, because it met his need than for the little children of Ninevah. God taught Jonah that He has compassion for every person He has knit together with His own hands.

In Hosea we saw the marriage of Gomer and Hosea. This marriage is a picture of Israel's relationship with God or the church's relationship with Jesus, as we are the bride of Christ. God's point is that we are all Gomers. We have all gone to other people or things for our comfort, security, love, affirmation and provision. We have all "clung to worthless idols" and "forfeit[ed] the grace that could be [ours]" (Jonah 2:8). This shows us that life is a level playing field. We are no better than our offenders are and no worse. God's response is not revenge, but compassion and redemption, buying us back from the slavery to which we willingly became bound.

GROUP EXERCISE

Materials needed:

1. Poster board
2. Catalogs and/or magazines
3. Glue

Have group members cut out pictures from magazines and catalogs and put them on poster board to represent idols that we worship. If you break into smaller groups for the discussion time, do this exercise during small group time. Have each group share their "idol" with the others at the end.

PRINCIPLE QUESTIONS

1. What "rights" did Jesus give up to become the human Messiah?
2. Why was God merciful to Ninevah?
3. What is the vilest adultery?
4. What did you learn about God's character this week?
5. What did you learn about judging others this week?

PERSONAL QUESTIONS

1. What right will you have to give up to forgive your offender?
2. Why do you not want God to be compassionate to your offender?
3. Where do you go (besides God) to get your comfort, security, love, affirmation and provision?
4. What has God freed you from?
5. How have you grown in forgiveness since the beginning of this study?

ANSWERS TO HOMEWORK

DAY 1

1. The same as Christ Jesus.
2. Give up self for others.
3. N/A
4. Jesus gave up equality with God, Lordship, and immortality. He also allowed Himself to be constrained by time and physical limitations such as hunger, thirst, fatigue, etc.

5. He was exalted to the highest place, given the Name above all names, every knee bowed to Him, every tongue confessed that He is Lord.
6. Having the same attitude.
7. Not pretentious, totally submissive to the Father's will, not having a focus on self, or glorifying self, but knowing your position in Christ (not the center of the universe, to be worshipped, but seated with Him in the heavenlies).
8. Humility—so sure of who you are and your worth that you don't have to prove it. Low self-esteem—so unsure of who you are and your worth that you have to find it in the eyes of others.
9. The motive is love and identity with Christ, not a motive of hunger for love or identifying with another human.
10. Not to put self first.
11. From time spent with Christ.
12. Having the same attitude, remembering our shared love for God, and a shared purpose/ commission in life.
13. N/A

DAY 2

1. To go to Ninevah and preach against it.
2. Was afraid God would be merciful.
3. On himself.
4. N/A
5. He did not think that Ninevah deserved God's compassion.
6. N/A

DAY 3

1. Gomer—an adulterous woman.
2. Jezreel, Lo Ruhamah, Lo Ammi.
3. Departing from the Lord.
4. To get things she "needed".
5. N/A
6. Showed her emptiness of idols, led her to the desert and wooed her and bought her out of slavery.
7. N/A
8. N/A
9. N/A
10. N/A
11. N/A

DAY 4

1. We find that our strength is lacking—reap what we sow.
2. N/A
3. His compassion is far greater than His anger, judgment or vindication.

4. That we acknowledge no God but Him.
5. Do not forget where you come from and how much you need the Lord.
6. N/A
7. N/A
8. He heals, loves us freely and turns away His anger.

DAY 5

Practical application

STEP 4—FORSAKING REVENGE

REVIEW

This week examined the fourth step in the forgiveness process—**forsaking revenge**. This step involves giving up revenge to leave room for the wrath of God. We can take revenge in various ways. Some are blatant, and others are not so obvious, even to ourselves. Revenge includes any actions that we take to make our offenders change that have not been directed by God. Whenever we are trying to change a person using our own devices, we are sure to fail and usually make things worse. We must make the choice to forsake revenge. We cannot wait for the good feelings to come and the negative feelings to disappear. We must do the action and the feelings will eventually follow.

Forsaking revenge is not encouraging God to take revenge while we enjoy the outcome. One time I was stuck in traffic getting very angry at all the cars passing by on the shoulder. Why should they get ahead while I obeyed the rules? Further up the road I saw a state patrol stopping every one of those people who passed on the shoulder. I rejoiced! And then God whispered in my ear, "You are taking revenge." Any time we rejoice over our enemy's tragedy, we are taking revenge.

Forsaking revenge is desiring God to motivate our offender to repentance. The purpose is not to see them judged, but to see them in right relationship with God. He may ask us to do things to encourage that repentance, but they may range from baking them a pie to taking them to court. We must remember that God is the surgeon, we are only His instruments. A surgical instrument left to itself can be very destructive, but in the hands of the surgeon it can bring healing and restore life.

Forsaking revenge, however, does not necessarily mean that we no longer feel anger. In actuality, forsaking revenge involves righteous anger and without it our love is dry and passionless. We often think that the opposite of love is hatred, but hate involves passion, just like love does. The opposite of love is indifference and apathy. When we hate our enemy, we can shift the focus of our passion from hating the person to hating the sin. When we are apathetic, we are passive, stagnant and stale. Our feelings have died and it takes incredible effort to resurrect them again.

GROUP EXERCISE

Materials needed:

1. Several large stones
2. Markers to write on the stones
3. A cross that stands or is attached to a wall

Each member of the group should pick as many stones as they need to represent the kinds of revenge they use. Using the markers, label each stone with the type of revenge. Have group members talk about the types of revenge they use and as they are ready, place each stone at the foot of the cross.

PRINCIPLE QUESTIONS

1. How do we leave room for God's wrath?
2. What are some differences between man's anger and righteous anger?
   Righteous anger leaves room for restoration.
   Righteous anger gets out of God's way.
   Righteous anger involves love.
   Righteous anger involves mercy.
   Righteous anger comes slowly and ends quickly.
   Righteous anger prevents evil, it does not promote evil.
3. What are the results of righteous anger and what are the results of man's anger?
4. How did Jehosephat fight his enemies?
5. In forsaking revenge, where is our focus to be?

PERSONAL QUESTIONS

1. What does seeking revenge do to you?
2. How righteous has your anger been?
3. What has been the result of your anger?
4. How are you fighting your enemies?
5. How is your trust level with God?

ANSWERS TO HOMEWORK

DAY 1

1. God's
2. In due time.
3. On His enemies.
4. His land and His people.
5. The Lord.
6. Deliver us.
7. Get out of the way.
8. 3 different interpretations:
   a form of judgment
   wearing a pot of burning coals on the head was an Egyptian sign of repentance
   heaping burning coals on the head was actually a blessing
9. N/A

DAY 2

Righteous anger leaves room for restoration	Romans 12:21
Righteous anger gets out of God's way	Romans 12:19
Righteous anger involves love	Luke 6:27-31
Righteous anger involves mercy	Hosea 1-3
Righteous anger comes slowly and ends quickly	James 1:19-20

DAY 3

1. Creating an idol.
2. Moses saw the calf Aaron made and people dancing.
3. Broke the tablets, called apart those who were for the Lord, prayed and allowed God to bring His consequences.
4. The Levites were set apart, 3,000 people died, and God forgave their sin.
5. Argued and complained against Moses and Aaron.
6. Prayed, but did not follow God's instructions because he was angry with the people.
7. He was angry with the people.
8. Moses did not trust God.
9. None
10. Still got water (God was faithful) but Moses lost the gift of going into the Promised Land.
11. To cleanse the temple and put it back to its original intent.
12. The temple courts or court of the Gentiles.
13. All nations.
14. The temple was cleansed, the Gentiles could worship again, the crowd was amazed, and the religious leaders wanted to kill Him.
15. God and the worship of Him.
16. N/A

DAY 4

1. Moabites, Ammonites and some Meunites.
2. Sought the Lord and proclaimed a fast for all Judah.
3. None
4. The Lord's
5. On God
6. It was His battle, not theirs.
7. The Lord
8. N/A
9. N/A
10. Singing praises to God.
11. He caused their enemies to fight amongst themselves and destroy each other.
12. Plunder that took 3 days to collect and peace on all sides.

DAY 5

Practical Application

STEP 5—DESIRING RESTORATION

REVIEW

Desiring restoration for our offenders is to long for restoration first between our offender and God, and then between our offender and others, including ourselves. There are four elements necessary to complete this step. First, we need to separate the person from the behavior. We can hate the sin and still love the sinner. This is related to Step 3 of becoming other-centered where we are fully aware of God's grace in our own lives and the result is humility and compassion on those around us.

The second element is imagining what the offender could be if he/she repented and was totally restored to God and man. For example, Chris' mother is living a lifestyle that is contrary to scripture. However, she was once very involved in church and had her heart set on the Lord. Her choices have grieved Chris and he has had to set some clear boundaries with her, especially in regards to her granddaughter. He was having difficulty with this step, until he invited his mom to a church social. As she was talking with other ladies from church, Chris had a flashback to when he was young and his mom was walking with the Lord. Through this, God restored his hope of seeing her in right relationship with Him again.

The third element is wanting change for the person's sake and not for our own. In the beginning of the forgiveness process we want to see change in our offender so that we can enjoy the outcome. We also want change for our own benefit—so we won't be hurt again. When our desire for change is selfishly motivated, we don't enjoy the change when it occurs. It doesn't happen the way we expect and we are always suspicious of the validity of the repentance. I have counseled many couples where there has been tremendous hurt. One spouse is praying for change in the other, and when it happens they are caught off guard and find that they are still stuck in the past. This is a clear sign that more forgiveness work needs to be done.

The fourth element of desiring restoration is yielding our heart to God for His protection and strength. I cannot work towards restoration and protect my back at the same time. As long as my walls of self-protection are firmly intact, restoration will be shallow at best. This step is where our trust in God is fully tested. We are not called to trust in our offender but in the Lord.

Highlight the 2 heart checks:

1. When we don't desire restoration, we are really no better than the one who has offended us, and we need to go back to Step 2.
2. Do I pray for God's blessing for my offender and rejoice when it comes, remembering it is God's kindness that leads to repentance?

GROUP EXERCISE

Materials needed:

1. A small rectangular box for each participant, such as a tissue box, with the top cut out to represent a gap between the victim and the offender.
2. Strips of construction paper cut to represent planks in a bridge.
3. Markers or pens

On the strips of construction paper, group members will write blessings for their offender and lay them across the top of the box to represent a bridge connecting the offender to the victim. Each participant can then share their bridge with their group.

Note: If you have a large group, it would be best to do this exercise during the small group time.

PRINCIPLE QUESTIONS

1. What involvement does God have in your offender's life?
2. What were Jesus' disciples like before they became His disciples? What risk did Jesus take in choosing them?
3. What did Jesus know about Judas?
4. What did you learn from Elisha's story?
5. How does God feel about those who choose destruction over obedience?

PERSONAL QUESTIONS

1. How did it make you feel to put your offender's name in Psalm 139?
2. How much of a risk are you willing to take in a relationship with your offender?
3. What is your motivation to see your offender repent?
4. What fear keeps you from wanting to restore with your offender?
5. What misunderstanding of God have you believed that has kept you from fully forgiving your offender?

ANSWERS TO HOMEWORK

DAY 1

1. He knows everything, where he goes, what he does and what he says.
2. He is wherever my offender goes.
3. He fearfully and wonderfully created him and knit him together in his mother's womb.
4. Long before he was ever born.
5. N/A

DAY 2

1. Matthew was a tax collector.
2. Jews did not like tax collectors and thought of them as sinners and traitors.
3. N/A
4. He was an apostle and he wrote the Gospel of Matthew. He died a martyr's death when he was murdered with a long handled ax that included a sword.
5. Three
6. He turned and looked straight at Peter.
7. N/A
8. He went out and wept bitterly.
9. No.
10. Peter was told to go with the men without hesitation and to preach to them.
11. They were saved and baptized in the Holy Spirit.
12. He did not hesitate to defend his actions.
13. N/A

DAY 3

1. He knew from the beginning.
2. Yes.
3. Yes.
4. No.
5. The other disciples could not tell who the betrayer was by Jesus actions.
6. No.

DAY 4

1. He trusted in God's protection.
2. The Lord.
3. N/A
4. N/A
5. God is in His holy temple and on His heavenly throne.
6. He is observing and examining men.
7. The Lord hates those who love violence.

8. The Lord loves justice.
9. When we devise a scheme of revenge, we usually get burned in the process.

DAY 5

1.	Psalms 37:13	e. Laughs at the wicked
2.	Romans. 5:8	j. Died for sinners
3.	Matthew 7:22-23	b. Will not allow to enter heaven
4.	Matthew 11:20-24	g. Will punish
5.	2 Peter 3:9	d. Doesn't want any to perish
6.	James 4:6	c. Resists the proud
7.	Luke 19:10	a. Saves the lost
8.	Luke 17:1-2	h. Will judge harshly
9.	Ezekiel 33:11	i. Takes no pleasure in the death of the wicked
10.	Ezekiel 18:21-23	f. Pleased when the wicked repent

STEP 6 PART I— CONFRONTING BELIEVERS

REVIEW

The difference between a goal and a desire is that a goal is something you have complete control over. If you fail to reach your goal, you can trace the failure back to a place where you did not follow through on a step(s) to reach your goal. A desire, however, is something where another person has at least partial control in the outcome. Therefore, the goal of confrontation can only be *providing the opportunity* for repentance. The desire can be to see the offender repentant, but the bulk of that outcome is in the control of your offender.

There are 5 motives you need to examine before you are ready to confront.

1. Are you looking for a place to vent your emotions? If so, go back to step 1.
2. Do you want an opportunity to place blame? If so, go back to step 2.
3. Are you using confrontation as a guise of concern, when really you just want the person to feel guilty? If so, go back to step 3.
4. Are you using confrontation as a means of punishment? If so, go back to step 4.
5. Are you expecting change from the confrontation? If so, go back to step 5.

Confrontation is an act of love. It means desiring the best for that person (repentance and restored relationships) and providing the opportunity for that to happen. Most of the time confrontation involves the sacrifice of confronting with pure motives, sacrificing pseudo-peace and superficial harmony and sometimes it is a sacrifice to even be in the presence of the offender. However, confrontation is also a means of solidifying the relationship, making it stronger than it was before, and an impartation of grace to your offender.

When we don't confront, we keep out the power of grace. We also rob our offenders of the opportunity to repent, for they may not even be aware of their sin or may not know how to express their repentance. We may even be allowing the person to remain in the cage of sin instead of giving them the key to escape the snare that has caught them.

Matthew 18 gives a good model for confronting other believers. First you are to go to them one on one. If there is no repentance, then you are to bring 2 or 3 witnesses to aid in the resolve. If there is still no repentance, then you are to bring the offender before a body of believers. If there is still no repentance, then you are to cut off the relationship, treating them as an unbeliever.

GROUP EXERCISE

Materials needed:

1. A roll of toilet paper
2. Narrator

Taking the roll of toilet paper, bind a volunteer with it until they are unable to move their arms or legs. The entire body does not have to be wrapped. The person can simply be wrapped around the torso and around the ankles.

The narrator should use the following script or an adaptation thereof.

This toilet paper represents the binding power of sin in our lives. It seems so little in the beginning but the more it is allowed in our lives, the stronger its power becomes. Confrontation is coming along and ripping a single cord of sin, exposing it for what it is – a binding power.

One at a time, have volunteers rip a single "cord" of toilet paper until the person is free enough to break the rest of the binding on their own. Then as a group, discuss the impact of sin on our lives, how it renders us impotent to free ourselves, the need for others to help us, how the person felt when freed and how this relates to confronting their offenders.

PRINCIPLE QUESTIONS

1. What does scripture say about the words of our mouth?
2. What was Nathan's concern when he confronted David?
3. What did Jesus' grace do to Peter? (Remember, Peter was repentant.)
4. What makes confrontation a loving thing to do?
5. What are the biblical steps for confrontation? (Matt. 18:15-17)

PERSONAL QUESTIONS

1. How have you used your words to hurt? How have you used your words to heal?
2. What are you hoping to see when you confront your offender?
3. What would grace from you do to your offender?
4. What has kept you from confronting your offender?
5. What have your confrontations been like in the past? If you knew then what you know now, how would they have been different?

ANSWERS TO HOMEWORK

DAY 1

Proverbs 12:18: "Reckless words pierce like a sword, but the tongue of the wise brings healing"

1. Not very big
2. It causes you to squint and blurs your vision
3. Pretty big
4. It blocks your vision
5. Our own issues cloud our vision.
6. N/A

Proverbs 15:18 "A hot-tempered man stirs up dissension, but a patient man calms a quarrel."

Jude 16 "These men are grumblers and faultfinders; they follow their own evil desires; they boast about themselves and flatter others for their own advantage."

Proverbs 10:11 "The mouth of the righteous is a fountain of life; but violence overwhelms the mouth of the wicked."

Proverbs 12:6 "The words of the wicked lie in wait for blood, but the speech of the upright rescues them."

DAY 2

1. It displeased the Lord.
2. The Lord sent him.
3. Nathan went to David out of obedience to the Lord. He had no hidden agendas or selfish ambition, his motives were pure. Because he loved the Lord and loved David, he desired to see his relationship restored to God.
4. N/A
5. The law required the death penalty for adultery and murder.
6. Nathan was more concerned about David's relationship with God than the law.
7. David's servants knew about the adultery and Joab knew about the murder.
8. No one else confronted David.
9. Nathan could have been killed for accusing the king or disagreeing with his behavior.
10. N/A
11. N/A

DAY 3

1. "Do you love Me?"
2. Jesus asked 3 times.
3. Peter denied Jesus 3 times.
4. "Feed my sheep."
5. It told Peter that Jesus trusted him to continue the work of teaching the gospel.
6. Jesus knew from the beginning that Peter would be an evangelist.
7. N/A

DAY 4

1. One who is caught in a sin.
2. No.
3. Not very easy.
4. To give the opportunity for restoration.
5. We have saved that person from death and a multitude of sins.
6. We leave that person in a death trap.
7. N/A
8. An open rebuke
9. N/A
10. Wounds from a friend.
11. An enemy multiplies kisses. In other words, they will flatter and condone behavior in order to better their own position.
12. N/A

DAY 5

1. A brother who has sinned against us.
2. When there is sin and it is against us.
3. No.
4. The offender and the "offendee."
5. If there is no repentance after the initial confrontation.
6. When there has been no repentance after the confrontation with 2 or 3 others present.
7. N/A
8. N/A
9. N/A
10. N/A
11. N/A
12. N/A

CONFRONTATION PART II— CONFRONTING UNBELIEVERS

REVIEW

Justice and forgiveness are not mutually exclusive. In fact, they are married to each other. Justice without forgiveness twists justice into retaliation, vengeance, or revenge. It distorts the godly characteristic of justice into a satanic means of having your own way. If God did not provide forgiveness for us, His wrath would totally annihilate us and He would be justified in His actions. But for us humans, to have justice without forgiveness would distort our nature into a demonic hunger for revenge. It is demonic in that the desire for revenge, not a passion for God, consumes us.

On the other hand, forgiveness without justice renders it impotent. The power in forgiveness lies in the knowledge that the offender deserves retribution yet does not receive it to the extent that he deserves. We as sinners must recognize the full extent to which we deserve to be punished and realize that God's forgiveness has rescued us from eternal damnation, void of any love or comfort. This will transform our inner being in a way that nothing else can. When we are unaware of the fullness of His wrath, we discount God's forgiveness as nothing more than a platitude.

The marriage of forgiveness and justice means that someone always pays the price. The question is who. When God forgives me, He pays the price for my sins. If I forgive my offender, I pay a relatively small price of discomfort and some pain, but Jesus paid the ultimate price because He absorbs my pain, sorrow and shame. Justice and forgiveness are joined at the cross.

Confrontation can make us painfully aware of the connection between forgiveness and justice. This is especially true when confronting unbelievers, those whom Proverbs calls fools. Fools do not appreciate confrontation and react in very negative ways when faced with their wrongdoing. In some cases the only way to confront the fool is in a court of law. However, you must be very aware of your motives in taking others to court and aware of the limited justice in this earth.

Finally, if you have gained nothing else from this study, I hope that you have learned that forgiveness is a trust issue with God. It does not matter whether the offender has repented or proven to be trustworthy. Complete forgiveness depends on complete trust in God to heal your pain, protect your heart and work on your offender.

GROUP EXERCISE

Materials needed:

1. Blindfolds
2. Obstacles

Set up an obstacle course. Pair group members and blindfold one person in each team. Ask the other person to lead the blindfolded person through the obstacle course. Afterwards, discuss with the group how it felt to depend on another to lead them and protect them. Then relate this experience with trusting God to lead and protect through the obstacles of life.

PRINCIPLE QUESTIONS

1. How are justice and forgiveness married to each other?
2. Who pays the price of forgiveness?
3. How can you expect a wise person to react to confrontation? How can you expect a fool to react to confrontation?
4. Can you forgive someone and still see him or her in a court of law?
5. What are the benefits of trusting the Lord for your conflict with your offender?

PERSONAL QUESTIONS

1. How has your sense of justice kept you from forgiving?
2. What price do you have to pay in forgiving your offender?
3. Recognizing the foolishness or wisdom of your offender, what is your tactic for confronting them?
4. Who do you need to take to court or what case do you need to drop?
5. How has this course stretched your trust in God?

ANSWERS TO HOMEWORK

DAY 1

Practical application

DAY 2

1. We are under a curse because we are subject to the law that condemns us because we cannot perfectly live by the law.
2. No.
3. He became cursed for us. He took on our curse.
4. Jesus Christ
5. We are justified through faith in Jesus
6. Forgiveness is when God's wrath is taken out on a willing substitute. Justice is when a wrong is rightly punished. The two work together in Jesus taking our punishment so we could be justified.
7. No one is available because we have all turned our backs against the Lord.
8. He was displeased that there was no justice.
9. He was appalled that there was no one to intercede.
10. God took matters into His own hands and provided the way for us.
11. God saved us through Jesus, He made us righteous through Jesus and He took His vengeance out on Jesus. But He will take His vengeance out on those who choose not to let Jesus take their place by becoming a Christian.
12. N/A

DAY 3

1. When you confront a fool, he will insult you, abuse you and hate you.
2. When you confront a wise man, he will love you, become wiser still and add to his learning.
3. N/A
4. N/A
5. Fools have no interest in making amends.
6. Have your expectations very low when confronting a fool.
7. Fools learn through painful consequences.
8. The wise learn through rebukes, corrections or confrontations.

DAY 4

1. Righteousness or justice.
2. N/A
3. God
4. Civil authorities are to do good for the people and to bring punishment to the wrongdoer.
5. The difference lies in the motive. I can take another to court because I want to protect others from harm (as in the case of drunk driving, child abuse, murder, etc.) I can also take others to court by allowing the civil authorities to do their job. However, we can also use the judicial system to exact revenge for us. When we want to see the person pay, that is revenge. When we want to see the person repent, that is forgiveness.

DAY 5

1. Evil people.
2. Fretting or worrying only leads to more evil.
3. The seven alternatives to worry are:
   <u>Trust</u> in the Lord (Verse 3)
   <u>Delight</u> yourself in the Lord (Verse 4)
   <u>Commit</u> your <u>way</u> to the Lord (Verse 5)
   Be <u>still</u> and wait <u>patiently</u> for God (Verse 7)
   Refrain from <u>anger</u> (Verse 8)
   Turn from <u>evil</u> (Verse 27)
   <u>Wait</u> for the Lord and keep <u>His</u> way (Verse 34)
4. God will:
   <u>Give</u> you the <u>desire</u> of your heart (Verse 4)
   Make your <u>righteousness</u> shine (Verse 6)
   <u>Cut</u> off evil men (Verse 9)
   Give you an <u>inheritance</u> (Verse 11)
   <u>Pierce</u> the heart of the <u>wicked</u> (Verse 14-15)
   <u>Uphold</u> the righteous (Verse 17)
   Break the <u>power</u> of the wicked (Verse 17)
   Provide <u>plenty</u> in times of need (Verse 19)
   Make your enemies <u>vanish</u> (Verse 20)
   Make your steps <u>firm</u> (Verse 23)
   <u>Uphold</u> you with His right <u>hand</u> (Verse 24)
   Love the <u>just</u> (Verse 28)
   <u>Protect</u> (Verse 28 & 33)
   <u>Saves</u> the righteous (Verse 39)
   Be a <u>stronghold</u> in time of trouble (Verse 39)
   <u>Delivers</u> you (Verse 40)

(Permission is granted to copy this page for ministry purposes.)

FEELING LIST

Abandoned	Afraid	Agitated	Angry	Annihilate
Anxious	Ashamed	Awful	Bad	Blamed
Belittled	Belligerent	Betrayed	Bewildered	Bitter
Broken	Browbeat	Cheap	Childish	Condemned
Confronting	Confused	Choking	Cold	Confined
Confused	Constricted	Cornered	Corrupted	Cowardly
Crazy	Criminal	Critical	Cureless	Cursed
Damaged	Damned	Deceitful	Defeated	Defenseless
Defiant	Defiled	Denied	Depleted	Depraved
Depressed	Deprived	Deserted	Desperate	Despised
Devalued	Disapproved	Devastated	Distressed	Disloyal
Disgraced	Disarranged	Disposed	Displaced	Discarded
Disordered	Disjointed	Dizzy	Doomed	I don't matter
Drained	Dreadful	Dumb	Dumbfounded	Dying
Embarrasses	Entangled	Evil	Excited	Exposed
Failure	Fake	Fatigued	Fault	Fearful
Flawed	Filthy	Foolish	Forgotten	Forsaken
Foul	Friendless	Frail	Frustrated	Gross
Guilt	Gullible	Hate	Hateful	Helpless
Homeless	Hopeless	Homosexual	Hopeless	Humiliated
Hysterical	Ignorant	Impaired	Impotent	Improper
Impending doom	Incompetent	Indecisive	Indecent	Indifferent
Inept	Inferior	Insignificant	Insufficient	In the way
Intimidated	Invalid	Jealous	Jittery	Judgmental
Lazy	Left out	Lewd	Little	Loathsome
Lost	Loser	Manic	Mistake	Mistreated
Misunderstood	Murderous	Nasty	Not wanted	Nervous
Numb	Obnoxious	Offensive	Oppressed	Overpowered
Overwhelmed	Outcast	Outsider	Out of Control	Paranoid
Pathetic	Panic	Perverted	Petty	Phony
Pressured	Powerless	Regretful	Rejected	Repugnant
Repulsive	Revengeful	Rubbish	Ruined	Sabotaged
Scared	Screwed up	Second class	Shameful	Sickening
Sinful	Sleazy	Slut/whorish	Smutty	Squashed
Squeezed	Stretched	Strife	Stupid	Suicidal
Suspicious	Tainted	Tarnished	Tentative	Tense
Terror	Tormented	Torn	Trapped	Trashy
Ugly	Unacceptable	Unappreciated	Unclean	Undecided
Unfit	Unloved	Unrighteous	Unsuitable	Untrusting
Unworthy	Valueless	Violent	Vulgar	Wasted
Weak	Weepy	Worried	Worthless	Wrong
Yucky				

(Permission is granted to copy this page for ministry purposes.)

RESOURCES

BOOKS

Inside Out	Larry Crabb
Hiding From Love	John Townsend
Boundaries	Henry Cloud and John Townsend
Dropping Your Guard	Chuck Swindall
Bondage Breaker	Neil Anderson
Victory Over the Darkness	
Getting Anger Under Control	
Co-Dependent No More	Melody Beattie
Love is a Choice	Robert Hemfelt
When People are Big and God is Small	Edward Welch
Blame it on the Brain?	
The Anger Workbook	Les Carter and Frank Minirth
The Worry Workbook	
Men's Secret Wars	Patrick Means
Anger is a Choice	Tim LaHaye and Bob Phillips
Addiction and Grace	Gerald May
A Passionate Pursuit of God	Tim Riter
Seduced by Success	Ann Kiemel Anderson
The Wounded Heart	Dan Allender
Bold Love	
Door of Hope	Jan Frank
Beauty for Ashes	John Coblentz

SEMINARS/GROUPS

Living Waters
12 Step Groups such as:
- Alcoholics Anonymous
- Narcotics Anonymous
- Al-Anon
- Overeaters Anonymous

(Permission is granted to copy this page for ministry purposes.)

RESOURCES *(continued)*

COUNSELORS

Elijah House	1-208-773-1645	www.elijahhouse.org
Focus on the Family	1-800-A FAMILY	www.family.org
His High Places	1-828-963-4866	www.hishighplaces.org
Meier New Life Clinics	1-800-NEW-LIFE	www.meiernewlifeclinics.com
Rapha	1-800-383-HOPE	www.raphacare.com
Theophostic Ministries	1-270-465-3757	www.theophostic.com

Broken People

- are overwhelmed with a sense of their own spiritual need.
- are willing to yield the right to be right.
- are humbled by how very much they have to learn.
- receive criticism with a humble, open spirit.
- are concerned with being real; what matters to them is not what others think but what God knows; are willing to die to their own reputation.
- once broken, don't care who knows or who finds out; are willing to be exposed because they have nothing to lose.
- are able to acknowledge specifics when confessing their sin.
- are grieved over the cause, the root of their sin.
- compare themselves to the holiness of God and feel a desperation for His mercy.

Proud People[8]

- focus on the failure of others.
- have to prove that they are right.
- feel confident in how much they know.
- are unapproachable or defensive when criticized.
- are concerned with being respectable, with what others think; work to protect their own image and reputation.
- want to be sure that no one finds out when they have sinned; their instinct is cover up.
- tend to deal in generalities when confessing sin.
- are concerned about the consequences of their sin.
- compare themselves with others and feel worthy of honor.

FORGIVE AND LIVE GROUP COVENANT

I, _____, covenant with my *Forgive and Live* group to do the following:

1. Begin and end on time in order to be good stewards of our time.

2. Complete the assigned study each week before the group session.

3. Pray regularly for my fellow group members.

4. Attend all group sessions unless circumstances beyond my control prevent attendance.

5. Participate openly and honestly in the group sessions.

6. Keep my discussion comments focused on the lesson as it relates to my circumstances and me.

7. Although my personal comments are vital to the discussion time, I will make them brief and to the point in order to allow everyone a chance to share, not being afraid of periods of silence.

8. Remember confidentiality is very important within the group.

9. Be attentive to other group members as they share, not judging differences in personality, circumstances or situations.

10. Be patient with other group members as God works in us all to make us what He wants us to be.

11. Be on time every_____ at _____.
                                  (day)   (time)

(Permission is granted to copy this page for ministry purposes.)

FORGIVE AND LIVE EVALUATION

1. What did you like best about *Forgive and Live*?

2. What did you feel needed improvement?

3. Was the material and discussion applicable to your life situation? Explain.

4. Was there adequate time for discussion and questions? Explain.

5. How effective was the homework in communicating the principles of forgiveness and making it applicable to your situation?

6. Would you take *Forgive and Live* again or recommend it to a friend?

ENDNOTES

[1] Analogy adapted from Dan Allender, "Abuse: Emotional, physical, and sexual"(part of the Basic Seminar presented by the Institute of Biblical Counseling in Charlotte, NC October, 1991).

[2] David Finkelhor et al., (Sexual Abuse in a National Survey, 1990) retrieved April 28, 2003 from One in Four: The Statistic of Sexual Abuse, http://home.btconnect.com/one-infour/index36.html.

[3] Allender, Dan, *The Wounded Heart* (Colorado Springs, CO: Navpress, 1990), 226.

[4] *NIV Study Bible*, (Grand Rapids, MI, Zondervan, 1985), 981.

[5] Ibid, 982.

[6] W.E. Vine, Merrill F. Unger, William White, Jr., *Vine's Complete Expository Dictionary of Old and New Testament Words*, (Nashville, TN, Thomas Nelson Publishers, 1996), 107.

[7] Robert L Thomas, ed., *New American Standard Exhaustive Concordance of the Bible*, (Nashville, TN, Holman Bible Publishers, 1981), 1643.

[8] Marriage Ministries International, (Winter 1996): 4.

[9] Allender, Dan, *The Wounded Heart* (Colorado Springs, CO: Navpress, 1990), 237.

9 781591 609056